Living the Presence of Now

JUDITH'S BOOKS

energywellness, 2004

I Brake for Butterflies, 2006

The Caregiver's Companion, 2010

Walking Between the Worlds, Book One, 2016

Walking Between the Worlds, Book Two, 2017

Living the Presence of Now, 2020

Judith's Insighttimer courses:
https://insighttimer.com/judithcampbell

Self-Care Healing Spaces of Grief and Loss

Living the Presence of Now with Self-Care Reiki Wellness

Living the Presence of Now

Through
Self-Care Reiki Wellness
and Yoga

Judith M Campbell
with guest Louise Murray

By living the presence of now,
we meet the living presence of now.

CONTENTS

Judith's Books — ii

Dedication — xi

In gratitude... — xiii

FOREWORD
The Healing Space of Living the Presence of Now — 5

CHAPTER ONE
Self-Care Reiki Retreat — 15

CHAPTER TWO
Manifesting Life Without Worry — 29

CHAPTER THREE
Becoming Authentic ... Living a Life of Truth — 47

CHAPTER FOUR
Anger as an Obstacle to Peace — 65

CHAPTER FIVE
Show Compassion to Yourself and Others — 83

CHAPTER SIX
Gratitude as a Way of Being — 105

CHAPTER SEVEN
Gratitude as a Way of Being — 123

CHAPTER EIGHT
A Self-Care Reiki Lifestyle and Sleep — 137

CHAPTER NINE
Resolving Root Causes of Obstacles to Create Peace — 153

CHAPTER TEN
The Healing Space of Now — 169

AFTERWORD
A Quick Review — 187

About the Author — 196

About the Yoga Instructor — 197

Endnotes — 199

"As a safe and gentle way to activate the parasympathetic nervous system via deep relaxation, Reiki has the potential to provide valuable support for a broad range of chronic health conditions. Research to date does not suggest that Reiki can cure any health condition, so it is not appropriate to regard Reiki as an alternative to allopathic medicine. Instead, Reiki should be regarded as a useful complement to conventional practices, especially for chronic illnesses where the use of drugs offers little benefit."[1]

DEDICATION

A wise person once said that everything we ever really need to know about in our life is already inside of us ...

Take what you will from this once said, wise person's view ...

From my perspective, it takes a journey with our spirit to unlock this wisdom that appears to be set to 'time-release' exactly when we are ready to receive it. Sometimes it releases when we need a push to discover life and sometimes it releases in moments of distress ... then, like the sun coming back into our world after days or weeks of darkness, we see what was before us all along and we are left wondering how we could have missed it. Simply stated, we weren't ready! We hadn't yet learned or experienced what was necessary, in order to see or understand what was before us all along.

I could add that a journey with Self-Care Reiki is very much like this. The teachings are there, waiting for us to discover their true meaning for each of us, as individuals ... yet, we need the passage of time for these teachings to unfold naturally for us ... to experience and live each one first hand as it applies to us ... as it returns us to our 'inner home' space. Such understanding cannot be rushed ... healing happens for us when we are ready to receive it ... open and trusting ... as we unlock the wisdom already within us.

I dedicate this book to ... and am eternally grateful for ... all the Self-Care Reiki students I have ever taught and will continue to teach in the years ahead. I have learned something from each one of you that has helped shape my own interpretation of the world; I am grateful for the privilege of knowing each of you and for the time spent in learning with each of you ... in the presence of now.

In the presence of now
We are one with the Universe,
We are one with her love,
We feel her healing energy
Mending us with peace ...

IN GRATITUDE...

To a most gracious YOGA Instructor, Louise Murray, for sharing your expertise in guiding us through five Yoga postures and to your son, Rob, for your photos.

Namaste, Louise and Rob!

and

To my adorable husband, David, for sharing some of his photos.

Thank you, Mr C!

and

To my very talented designer, Magdalene Carson, of New Leaf Publication Design, who has skillfully turned this work into what you are holding in your hand.

Thank you, Mag!

Living the Presence of Now

Come,
Linger awhile
In the presence of now,
The coolness of shade
In morning's glade.

Come,
Rest awhile,
Touch
The presence of now,
Take everything in,
Promise …
To return again.

The Healing Space of Living the Presence of Now

You have travelled too fast over false ground;
Now your soul has come, to take you back.[2]

— John O'Donohue

The power of now, is an expression made famous following the publishing of Eckhart Tolle's popular book[3] by the same name. For one, such as myself, working in energy healing since 1993, the power of now can mean any number of things. So, before you move into the reading of this book, I have decided to pare down this expression into sound-bites of sorts, to create a discussion on one very special aspect of 'now.' Specifically, this is the *'living presence'* of now ... as enjoyed within a lifestyle of Self-Care Reiki.

As I write this, the entire world is attempting to emerge following the Covid-19 Pandemic lockdown. The power of now could never be more meaningful for each of the stages imposed upon world citizens, to try to stop the spread of this virus. The power of now, in terms of self-isolation, has shown up as being critical. Countries that took this step too late have had more deaths per capita population than those that moved sooner ... historical science has shown the exact moment it was critical to take this step to avoid needless deaths ... *the power of now,* being a huge factor, *in hindsight.*

Testing to locate the virus ... equally critical to this process ... and when found, the follow-up quarantine and tracking of contacts, essential to identify whether they have been infected also and who their contacts have been ... *the power of now.*

5

Simple hand washing after touching anything outside one's own home, to stop the self-contamination and the potential spread of the virus. The power of now has been critical here as well. There's no point in washing contaminated hands after they have been on your face. The time to disinfect is immediately following potential contamination ... *the power of now*.

Social distancing to stop the spread once the virus is known to have arrived in any locality, shutting down workplaces, schools, places of worship, etc., where people congregate in close proximity ... *The power of now* is the taking of these steps at the critical moment, before the virus arrives in the community. For science has indicated it will surely come!

There simply is no argument about these necessary steps that are part of the curtailing of a microscopic virus, more powerful than the most severe destructive weapons of any one country's arsenal ... powerful enough to wipe out populations, if not stopped in its tracks ... *the power of now.*

Countries all over the world have taken the steps to try to fight this invisible enemy of the people that seeks out their populations' most vulnerable, showing no compassion to young or old, disabled or able, colour or creed ...

This is the backdrop with which everyone in the world can now identify, having lived and experienced a version of these 'power of now' details ...

What I want to discuss, bears no resemblance to any of this.

I want us to look at the *presence* of now. **'Presence' is very much a form of power,** as you will come to see. There are no words to adequately describe the presence of now, however, there are feelings to describe the living of it.

Within each 'now moment' of living our life, we can either tune out the living moment as our 'now reality,' or we can tune in to its 'now reality.' **Tuning in, is where the power is, in terms of presence.** And by 'presence,' I refer to the way that the energy of the moment *feels* ... not the way you think it might feel. **The presence of now relaxes your cognitive mind by reminding**

you of your beautiful array of senses, experienced through your emotion ... acknowledging how you feel in any given moment ... how you are *living* that moment ... whether or not you are *connecting to the presence of that moment through your feelings.* To make this quite simple, I will use an example from nature because it is familiar to everyone, the sunrise:

What's so important about a sunrise? It happens every day. Big deal!

Big deal, indeed. *The presence of now* would have you up at first light, *feeling* the anticipation of the sunrise ... then *feeling* your connection with its first rim of golden light rising above the horizon — aware of how your body's changing energy *feels* as you watch without taking your eyes away for even one second, until the full globe of gold lifts away from the horizon and begins to take its place in the sky. The entire experience is one of *living* the presence of now through your constant connection to each moment and changing phase of the sunrise, *fully tuned in to how the sunrise feels in your body / mind / spirit and soul.*

You get the idea ... the sunrise's presence of now is not just about the golden ball, whose presence we anticipate ... or about the full spectrum of vibrant colours that precede it, then diminish in intensity as the sun has lifted ... or about any clouds that might be in the sky at the time of sunrise that absorb the colours and allow colour to assume shape in the eastern sky. **The presence of now extends beyond noticing how every moment of the sunrise feels throughout our body and mind, our spirit and our soul. It is about our complete sense of openness to receive these sensations of oneness throughout the entire experience, oneness with the sun, the colour, the clouds, etc., with no separation.**

But, what if you cannot see? ... what if you do not have the sense of sight? ... how might you experience the presence of now as it pertains to the sunrise? The pre-sunrise presence of now is also *heard* in the bird activity any time before and following first light. Various species chime in their collective calls to announce the arrival of a new day. This announcement is accompanied by a change in the way the air feels on the skin, and in the sound and sense of stillness versus a breeze that often follows sunrise ... *The presence of now does not require our sense of sight or our sense of hearing to experience the sunrise. Rather, it gifts us with an ability to make a living connection with the full spectrum of energy as nourishment of our body, mind, spirit and soul.*

Seemingly oblivious to this, the completely silent ascent of light begins; the heat and light source for the entire world ... slowly rising to take its timely, visible place in a timeless and eternal universe ... *the heat and light can be felt energetically by the body,* despite one's inability to see or hear the birds that call for its arrival ... *the presence of now.*

On the ground, the sun's light creates shadow ... magically changing with the time of day and time of year ... reflected through length, exactness of positioning and science of angles ... *the presence of now* ... ever changing ... ever present ... ever miraculous ... *the sun's rays are felt by the sighted and unsighted, the hearing and hearing impaired ... the able and disabled alike.* **The sun's presence of now miracle knows no barrier ... it belongs to everyone ... it is life-changing when experienced as the *presence of now*** ... its presence to us holds such power ... always meeting us exactly where we are ... able to cast our very own image against any background where we might be standing, or sitting, or walking. In the presence of now, *we sense and feel a connection with the sun that has created our image* ... from more than 92,900,000 miles away[4] ... *such power in this living presence of now.*

Also on the ground, the sensitive observer witnesses this miracle of morning sunrise ... wantonly experiencing *the presence of now* in the way he or she feels in *this* moment of now, and *the next* moment of now, and so on until the moments of now are all joined into a living sense of permanence within ... something that is familiar, safe and secure ... something that shelters and protects ... while *feeding the soul* with *an eternal sense of 'home' through the presence of now* ... *nourishing the spirit* with a loving and

eternal presence of now ... *calming the mind* with an eternal sense of belonging in the presence of now ... and *relaxing the body,* with reassurance in the eternal presence of now ... *all felt in the split-second moment of now sunrise ... is this sense of eternal presence ... this power of now.*

Contrast this with one who sleeps through this miracle, or who is physically present for the miracle without being tuned in to experience it ... to feel and know its presence of now or its power. Another day passes for this person, another day of missing out on the presence of now, and yet, **this miracle is available to absolutely every living thing on planet earth.**

As we break down any topic into its multidimensional potential to discover the presence of now, an entirely new perspective emerges. It is like we remove blinders from our intellect. All facets of our five senses are challenged as are our senses beyond these, where **we awaken to our intuitive abilities** *to experience the presence of now through the reality of our genuine feelings* ... and **to acknowledge these feelings honestly as they apply to the reality of now, the power and presence of now.**

In the presence of now — *our 'inner home' space* **— we feel one with** *all that is* ... we feel a part of the sunrise living within us ... a part of the morning light and the bird songs announcing the coming of the sun ... we feel a part of the opening flowers that closed at sunset and now re-open to receive the light from the sun ... a part of the moistness of the morning air and the stillness ... we feel a part of the observer who stands in awe watching the miracle of the sunrise and a part of the one who misses it ... we know what we have witnessed and we know the sensation of missing it or even being oblivious to it ... this too, is *the living presence of now.*

Why am I introducing a book on Self-Care Reiki with these ideas? What have they got to do with Reiki?

The Journey of Self-Care Reiki is a journey that will lead you back to your 'inner home' space ... where *all that is* lives timelessly within you, waiting to be reunited with the fullness of your body, mind, spirit and soul ... it is a 'home space' where things like worry and anger do not exist and the truth about who you are is undebatable and secure ... it is a 'home space' where love and peace prevail such that life is lived with compassion and gratitude for the moment and power of now in *the ever-changing feeling of the presence of now. This is the Journey of Self-Care Reiki.*

In Self-Care Reiki Meditation, we have a practice that is all-inclusive, it can be used by anyone and everyone throughout the world. It is a practice that is completely natural, for it uses our hands to facilitate energy flow in our body, in an attempt to harmonize and heal as it guides us back to our 'inner home' space.

As we experience our Self-Care Reiki Meditation practice through a conscious awareness of *the living presence of now,* **we are introduced to an added dimension of Source energy ... of focused awareness that nourishes us holistically in** *the presence of now* **and reminds us of our inner home space.**

Returning to our inner home space is like stepping into our most comforting imagery of 'home,' with no obstacles to distract us ... and just as the sensation of 'being present to the sunrise' brings us comfort, **in living the presence of now we open to our own internal sunrise ...** our ability to experience the energy that we are receiving and sharing through our hands, with all parts of our body, mind, spirit and soul ... *the living presence of now.*

And, like the sun reaching out to us to bring us light and Source energy wherever we are in the world, Self-Care Reiki highlights our own shadows that separate us from our 'inner home' space in the presence of now, such that we can react and alter our behaviours that instil darkness ... *the living presence of now.*

When we practice Self-Care Reiki as meditation with a living sense of the presence of now, Reiki's energy lights up our inner home space. Like the sun lights up the sky, Reiki highlights colour in our day and helps us focus on the positive, enhancing our ability to feel and acknowledge our own inner colour and light ... *the living presence of now.*

If we can envisage the concept of 'now' as a long line, we will soon realize that there is no beginning and no end ... the sense of 'now' is still 'present' as we immerse ourselves in the memory of something important in our past; it is as though we are present to the time the memory represents. Similarly, we can place ourselves into the future.

As you will come to realize in the pages ahead, the self-care practice of Reiki is preparing us to live our lives in peace. It is preparing us to witness the sunrise rather than sleeping through it, and to witness it with the full intensity of its pure presence. We learn to do this by letting go of all sorts of common ways of living with negative emotions that interrupt peaceful ways of living and thinking.

The result of a lifestyle of peace means that should one receive a diagnosis of cancer, for example, rather than investing time in fear and worry about the outcome, you choose to envisage the outcome through the lens of positivity. **Your inner peaceful presence will allow you to feel gratitude for a full recovery even before you have begun treatment** ... and to hold this positive vision all along the way on your journey to recovery.

The presence of now is essentially the feeling you have from complete presence to whatever you are living or witnessing in this very moment ... the good the bad and the ugly. ***The challenging aspect of engaging 'presence' as a living entity requires that you continue to acknowledge the feeling of your inner home space of peace amidst the reality of whatever it is you are living;*** *to see the good that can come out of social unrest, to see health where there is sickness, hope where there is despair, compassion where there is anger, and love where there has been abandonment.*

One means of reaching this sense of a living presence of now is through a Reiki Meditation practice. By using Self-Care Reiki gentle touch as we meditate, we have a perfect combination of intention to both find and feel the complete

peace that is possible within us ... then to live this healing space of peace each day, in the presence of now. As you will see in the pages that follow, this was the intent of Reiki's founder, that all who practice might find this peaceful space within, amidst whatever chaos surrounds you; this is the space of Anshin Ritsumei, the feeling of peace within chaos, *in the living presence of now.*

> *In the presence of now*
> *The Universe speaks*
> *Of love and of peace.*
> *In the presence of now*
> *I am one with the Universe;*
> *I speak*
> *Of love and of peace.*
>
> — Judith

Overcome space, and all we have left is Here.
Overcome time, and all we have left is Now.[5]

— Richard Bach

CHAPTER ONE

Self-Care Reiki Retreat

A Self-Care Reiki practice trains us to live a 'presence of now' reality, to enjoy the full benefits of the human experience. By learning to remain connected with our Source energy, we meet *the living presence of now* ... the unseen, yet very potent 'something more' aspect of our human potential. Teaching us to experience this and become mindful of all of Reiki's energy-healing benefits, one's daily Self-Care Reiki Meditation practice is fundamental. Here, time stands still. We develop a sense of the presence of now and learn to practice and live this in all areas of our life. In our first chapter, you are encouraged to create a healing space within your home that will call to you to retreat into it daily; to further develop this living sense of presence that you already know to be powerful in your life. Having the foundational 'props' can be as simple as an unused corner of a room, or a spot on the ground beneath a favourite tree outdoors, either of which is comforting and inviting. A simple Reiki exercise is introduced that can be used for private and group meditation.

Everything in the Universe possesses
Reiki energy, without exception.
We are Reiki already!

— **Mikao Usui**

… from notes taken by students of Reiki's founder, Mikao Usui,
shared by Author and Reiki Master Teacher Hiroshi Doi,[6]
in an interview with Frans Stiene. [7]

Hello and welcome! Whether this is your first exposure to Reiki or whether you are already a practitioner, **may the Source energy of Reiki bring you closer to the *special* place that lives within you that is open, ready to receive, and trust ... your 'inner home' space.** I recommend you read only one chapter per sitting, to allow the information to gently seep through you to a deeper place of understanding.

I would like you to imagine your 'outer home' — the place where you live, as a retreat setting. If you do not have a reading or meditation corner already, this is an opportunity to create your own special space for these activities. **Sometimes, all it takes to create a retreat-like space, is to turn a chair around to face *out* a window rather than *in* to your room;** this will offer an entirely new vista for you.

Into this space, please place a candle you can light as you spend time here. The simple lighting of a candle has the ability — in its moment of lighting — to connect you with the conscious presence of 'something more' that is beyond you, *yet within you ... present ... yet unseen.*

When a candle is lit with the awareness of *the presence of now*, its quiet stillness of light prepares you to receive the teachings this moment offers. (We'll come back to this in a moment.) Add to this, a journal by your side, to capture any random thoughts that come as you are inspired by a new idea or memory that turns into a teaching for you. A meditation shawl or soft blanket will befriend you in your retreat space as well. **These items help to set the tone for self-care comfort and relaxation.**

Finally, a little meditation music will allow you to settle in and embrace a more relaxed pace as you read. Ear buds tuned into meditation music from a free app such as Insight Timer[8] will bring all of this preparation together. I will offer suggestions for listening, while knowing you may prefer to use your own meditation music or simply enjoy the silence. Today's offering is a short, peaceful favourite of mine from Insight Timer, called Golden OM,[9] and perhaps an invitation to relax into the divine energy of the Universe ... all that lies waiting for you to discover along the way of your reading. (Hint: play it on low volume.)

The more you observe *the living presence of now* in any of your actions, the closer you will come to your *inner home space,* where your truth and authentic self reside. **Your journey of Self-Care Reiki has already begun, and is leading you there ...**

Self-Care Reiki Meditation

At the beginning of each chapter — after you have selected your music, if you wish to have music — we will take a moment for you to light your candle, followed by a simple exercise to help you center, using what is known in Reiki, as Gassho. This word literally means to bring 'two hands together.' Usually, this position is held in front of the heart centre, with your palms facing each other and touching, while focusing on the tips of your middle fingers. Then relax your arms and shoulders. Our time in Gassho, is an opportunity to create an intention for your reading and 'retreat' time. So let's take this next moment for you to do this now, closing your eyes as you create your intention ... taking a breath to help you center ... then open your eyes again.

Now that we are ready to continue, we'll get you started right away on **self-care gentle touch, the corner stone of a Self-Care Reiki practice.** In each reading retreat session, we will use a different gentle touch position.

Today we will begin with a more relaxed finger-tip version of the Gassho position. This time, I would like you to hold the same position you have just used, with your finger tips only, then lower your arms and rest your hands on your lap, on the midline of your body, making sure you are completely comfortable.

Again, that's two hands together at your finger tips, relax your arms and rest your hands — very simply — on your lap; then I invite you to close your eyes and just take a few moments to begin to relax into the sounds of your music or the silence ... take several slower and fuller breaths ... and remain in this quiet space for as long as feels comfortable to you ... and when you are ready, open your eyes ... and continue ...

Reflection

How was this for you? Please notice how you are feeling before continuing. You may wish to write your experience in your journal.

Our continuing self-care gentle touch position as you read, is to now **gently touch** one hand against the midline of your torso, as you hold your book or device to read.

The most frequently asked question I receive about Reiki is simply: *What is Reiki?*

My answer? Reiki is energy.

Beyond this initial response and as a more encompassing way of answering this question:

- *Reiki is healing energy,*
- *Reiki is meditation,*
- *Reiki is peace,*
- *Reiki is love and compassion,*
- *Reiki is gratitude,*
- *Reiki is a way of being,*
- *Reiki is mindfulness training,*
- *Reiki is our relationship with ourselves, with one another and with the Universe,*
- *Reiki is an energy that is alive, that heals, that awakens when we open ourselves to it,*
- *Reiki is an energy that guides ... guides us **through** our opening awareness **towards** those things we need, and **away from** those things that may be harmful,*
- *Reiki is life-changing,*
- *Reiki guides us to live in the presence of now.*

A Self-Care Reiki Meditation practice combines the additional energy flow of Reiki through hands resting on the body while meditating, combined with stillness. Evidence-based effects of meditation can easily be found on the internet in many scientific reports and articles. The co-founder of the Insight Timer Meditation app, Christopher Plowman, refers to the mission of Insight Timer as being that of consciousness raising globally, another huge benefit of meditation. He actually suggests that people not be thrown off the idea of meditation and just learn to sit quietly for ten or fifteen minutes a day like a "time out," to simply learn to be still."[10]

Beyond scientific evidence that this energy is real, I recognize that there are those who do not believe in anything they cannot see. And yet, pets and plants are affected positively by the energy of Reiki. And from my experience in working with this energy for almost three decades, people who know nothing about Reiki are affected positively also. In my ten-year practice as a Hospice Volunteer Reiki Practitioner, I have learned, first hand, how Reiki offers hospice clients much comfort from their stress. When offered to the dying, a short session of hands-on Reiki gentle touch can remove the fear of death and allow the person to end their life's journey in peace.

So, from my own experience, I can safely add to my answer, above, that Reiki is healing energy that connects us with *'something more'* ... with what I am calling, *the living presence of now.*

Self-Care Reiki's energy goes to the places in your body / mind / spirit / soul that need it the most without needing to be directed there! Reiki's dynamic energy searches out imbalance to calm, restore and heal; it awakens, and it guides. Reiki helps to balance emotions when they are on overdrive, and open you to coping strategies to deal with your daily challenges. **Self-Care Reiki is the energy potential you bring to everything you do.**

In the words of Phyllis Furomoto, a former descendant and bearer of the Reiki's original Usui Shiki Ryoho lineage, "**Reiki is love** that brings us closer to who we are as a human being as we surrender to its energy *without* a specific intention for healing."[11] **This is key to understanding Reiki, and what makes this form of energy healing different from other energy therapies that work directly with intention.**

Reiki connects us with a special space inside of us through gentle touch — as you are experiencing right now, *I hope.* **Gentle Touch of Self-Care Reiki,** when combined with taking time to sit down and be quiet ... then slowing the breath ... *in the presence of now* ... **becomes *Reiki Meditation.***

In addition to gentle touch and the meditative aspect of Self-Care Reiki, Reiki's founder, Mikao Usui, added **mindfulness coaching** through what he called 'Reiki Precepts.' We will spend five of our chapters discussing the Precepts, beginning with our next session, where we will speak about worry as one of the behaviours or habits that gets in the way of feeling inner peace.

Also included in these next five chapters, is the link with each of the natural elements as well as a yoga posture that exemplifies how to incorporate a yoga practice with Self-Care Reiki. An awareness of these natural linkages fortifies our ability to sense inner peace and to heal. My gratitude goes to guest Yoga

Instructor, and Yogini, Louise Murray, who will illustrate and instruct each posture.

Inner peace is a huge part of the 'something more' in our life's potential way of being. **When we stray from this potential, we *disconnect* from this wondrous aspect of our humanity**... and in disconnecting, we become less and less authentic ... forgetting who we truly are inside.

The *something more* aspect of ourselves that we cannot see or touch, opens us to an expanded view of ourselves and of our relationship with *all that is.* And by *all that is,* I refer to our relationship with the energies of the Universe that *surround us and are within* us at all times.

Our conscious awareness of how we might be connected to or affected by elemental energies, **moves us** from an insular view of our relationship with the world outside of ourselves **to an expanded view of who we truly are inside. By learning to quiet our minds and our bodies, we can hear the inner voice of 'something more' we all have within us that struggles to be heard above the din of daily life** ... this is our intuitive voice that guides us towards and away from those activities and people that can help or harm. *It guides us towards living and feeling the presence of now in all we do and in all we are.*

So, much of our Self-Care Reiki focus and way of being, is learning to listen to this inner guidance ... to focus less on egocentric needs and more on the aspects of life that truly matter and make a difference, such as our awareness of others ... awareness of the need to show compassion as a normal way of being, compassion towards ourselves, towards others and to all that has life, including animal life, plant life and the environment ... this is a huge component of our relationship with the universe, with *all that is.*

Usui Sensei developed a set of Precepts as a very practical aspect of Reiki to help us with this. We will be discussing these Precepts fully in the next six chapters so that you can relate to how they can be used to help you focus on the things that really matter. **The Precepts will help you let go of fixed and outdated habits, attachments and beliefs that**

no longer serve you. As you liberate yourself from energies (behaviours and attitudes, etc.) you have outgrown, you will be more open to receive new ways of living your life in the energy presence of now.

Self-Care Reiki immerses us in the energy of our innermost self which we will describe in various ways in this book. We sometimes think of this energy as a 'sacred space' of spiritual energy. We may also think of this as our 'inner universe,' uniting us with the living and infinite aspects of ourselves we have not known before, or perhaps have forgotten. *Were we to live from our inner universe of sacred space, we would not require the guidance of Precepts to help us, we would simply trust that our life would unfold for our highest good. This, in truth, is our ultimate objective of a self-care practice that unites us with our sacred space. The reality is, however, that the majority of us will need some help to remain steadfast to this space, and hence the reason for this book you are holding in your hand ...*

Connected to this inner energy, is our 'outer universe,' the equally infinite and timeless part of ourselves that contains the healing energies found within the natural elements that live all around us. **A key aspect of our Self-Care Reiki energy awakening, therefore, is becoming mindfully aware of this Universe —** *the something more of our existence* **— whose energies reside in constant relationship with us** ... it is where our living awareness of these energies meet, *in the sacred presence of now,* that healing happens *within us ...*

We carry the possibility of the sacred within us at all times, allowing us to see the best in others, and in ourselves, within the sacred space that surrounds us. Perhaps this is the space of something more, of pure consciousness, wherein we exercise this ability to see and acknowledge all that is good, and sacred.

Several years ago, I opened my writing of a book on body, mind and spirit wellness with a poem[12] that had been insightfully received while on a Reiki retreat some weeks earlier. I am repeating the poem in this book fourteen years later — two life cycles later — because *I finally get it! We need the passage of time for spiritual teachings to unfold meaningfully and to live each one first hand as it applies to us as individuals.*

Take your time and let the words of each line and each verse sink in to your awareness ...

I am in the mists of time
I am in the silent sound of waters
I am in the thunderous sounds of oceans
I am in the gentle breezes and the tumultuous hurricanes
I am in all that is.

I find myself only as I awaken to this level of consciousness: pure
*   consciousness,*
This level of consciousness that acknowledges
This level of consciousness that knows
This level of consciousness that understands
That I am in all that is.

Here, in this place of pure consciousness, healing is in the past.
Healing is in the present, and
Healing will be in the future.
For there will be times when I will forget my past;
There will be times when I will forget
That I am in all that is.

And then, something
Will guide me back to the place inside of me that remembers
When time began
And I will once again know that I am in all that is.

Have you ever experienced a deja-vu moment ... or a sensation
that lifts you outside of your being for a moment to see yourself
as 'an observer' of your life, or to understand something instinc-
tively, yet for which you have no experience? In some respects, this poem speaks to such phenomena, while reinforcing the idea that there is so much more to our lives than what we see or understand. At the time of writing this poem, I had just received one of these experiences in which I acknowledged myself — *my inner self, the part of me that is me* — as being age-less ... it was an awesome sensation.

Self-Care Reiki takes us beyond our physical body we see and leads us inward, to our inner universe, the invisible parts that make up a large part of who we truly are.

Self-Care Reiki reconnects us to these sacred and eternal parts of us, our spirit and soul ... **our lifeline back to Source energy,** *of all that is.*

Self-Care Reiki allows us to grow into the potential of our true and authentic selves — with a lifestyle that is supported by the energies of the Universe, **understanding that** *in the presence of now, we are a part of all of this — a part of all that is* — **and all that is, is** *actually* **a part of us.** This is especially important when we feel we have lost our way.

Self-Care Reiki helps us learn to trust, and for those who have lost this ability because of being hurt by life's circumstances, learning to trust again can be a long and engaging process. Self-Care Reiki will help you get there.

Self-Care Reiki helps us remember who we truly are — and in remembering, **to realize that what we might be searching for** *outside* **of ourselves ...** *is already within us.*

Self-Care Reiki, as lifestyle, assures us that we are already there ... we're already home ... and that this inner place we 'feel' as 'home' can not only bring comfort to us personally, it can grow out from us such that *by our presence alone,* **we can help others find their way back home to themselves also!**

Have you ever sat with a person and found yourself relaxing ... just being in their presence? It may have nothing to do with the conversation. It is about their energy. **It is the energy of** *their* **presence that surrounds** *you* **with the comfort you need at that moment** — without the person even realizing the effect he or she is having on you.

Going more deeply into this sensation, the familiar comfort of their energy is not only recognized by your body and mind, it is also acknowledged by your spirit / soul, like a stored memory of nourishing energy. This is a very practical suggestion of what could be meant by the expression, 'something more;' it doesn't have to mean something that represents a 'god-like' spiritual being. **'Something more' can simply be the spiritual** aspect of the one with whom you are sitting, or living, or loving ... whose energy your own spirit recognizes, like an old friend, and relaxation ensues ... allowing you to reconnect with your own inner universe again, *your inner home.*

'Something more,' is also a sensation you may experience in many other facets of life, as you feel overcome by music, for example, by the beauty within a child's newborn face, or by the sound of a voice you are yearning to hear. **'Something more' can become a living aspect of your daily life as you move in and out of awareness of how these special moments affect you in the presence of now. You will begin to understand just how much *you are in all that is* and how *all that is, is also in you!***

Bottom Line Teaching

A Self-Care Reiki practice trains us to live in a 'presence of now' reality, to enjoy the full benefits of the human experience, by remaining connected with our Source energy — with something more — *in the presence of now.*

Who can benefit from Self-Care Reiki? **Everyone!** Just as your hands instinctively go to comfort a hurt after an injury, without having to think about it, you can think of Reiki's self-care touch as a 'proactive way' to restore or replenish your energy on a daily basis. **Daily, Self-Care Reiki will help to keep your energy balanced as you continue to give of yourself to others, to your work and to all you do and are.**

Exploring how a Self-Care Reiki practice can influence your life right now and into the future is really what this book is about. You will have the opportunity to try out several self-care activities and test how each affects you. In our next chapter, we will be looking at the first of Mikao Usui's mindfulness coaching, or affirmations, regarding his first precept about worry.

As you have been reading with one hand held against the mid-line of your torso, are you finding this comforting?

As we end our first session together, I invite you now to read the last two paragraphs below, and then put your book or device down and allow yourself to enjoy a few additional moments of comfort.

Note: You can also find an expanded version of this following practice on Insight Timer, under my name and the meditation title: **Reiki Presence.**[13]

Place the palms of your two hands together in Gassho position again, and bring your focus to your middle finger tips — pointing upwards now. Gassho is used for calm and comfort in personal and group Reiki meditation, and in receiving a Reiki attunement.[14]

So, for another few moments, please settle in to this Self-Care Reiki Meditation position ... with your hands placed comfortably in front of the midline of your chest ... breathe more slowly so your shoulders can relax and soften ... then continue to breathe more slowly ... and deeply ... a few times ... allowing each exhale to be a little longer than the inhale ... feeling the beautiful energy of stillness that sur-rounds you ... and resides within you in your own sacred space as you relax with your breath ... *the energy of stillness that has the potential to connect you with the energy flow of something more ... inside you ...* nourishing you in this quiet and peaceful energy ... flowing in your body ... *in the presence of now ...* and remain in this position for as long as feels right for you today ...

Until next time, when you rejoin me in this sacred space, please be gentle with yourself. Namaste!

CHAPTER TWO

Manifesting Life Without Worry

Who doesn't worry about something, some of the time?

A Self-Care Reiki practice trains us to live without fear in a 'presence of now' reality by learning to stop worrying as a way of being, setting an example for all with whom we share our life to do the same. As you release the worry habit, you are closer to finding your 'inner home.'

In this chapter, the Universal Life Force of the Earth Element is introduced as an aspect of 'something more,' that can assist in your energy flow as you do your hands-on practice. The first Self-Care Reiki precept, *Just for today, do not worry,* is introduced to counter worry habits. You will learn how Self-Care Reiki Meditation can help you partner with the Earth Element to imagine a different outcome from worry images, grounding you instead, in healing energy flow of the secure and foundational earth. A Self-Care Reiki Touch position will help you work with this concept. A simple Yoga posture is introduced at the end of the chapter to demonstrate how Reiki, Yoga, the Root Chakra and the Earth Element combine to enhance your self-care practice, and help you find the healing space of your 'inner home,' firmly rooted *within you.*

Draw alongside the silence of stone
Until its calmness can claim you.
Be excessively gentle with yourself.[15]

— John O'Donohue

Hello again! I hope you are comfortably seated within your retreat space of your home, with all of your preparations we discussed last time having been made to allow your reading time today to be very special for you. As background music, you might be interested in listening to the first in a sound-healing series of Tibetan Singing Bowls that correspond with the chakra system. If so, I recommend you begin today with the Root Chakra sound meditation,[16] available on Insight Timer, since we will be discussing the healing, natural earth element that supports the root chakra.

Did you enjoy the healing space of the Gassho meditation at the end of our first chapter? To centre and prepare for reading this chapter please light your candle, then resume the Gassho position and set your intention for your reading retreat, then enjoy a moment with eyes closed, before beginning our time together today ...

Self-Care Reiki Meditation

You may wish to record the following meditation (and others in subsequent chapters) so that you can listen to your own voice saying the words ... you may find more benefit from the experience by doing this ... read slowly, allowing yourself time for slower breaths at the appropriate times. (This will allow you to listen again in the future if you wish ...)

Let's take a moment for you to imagine a beautiful setting somewhere in the world where you feel particularly drawn and 'at home' ... a place that almost seems to call to you at times, even creating a sense of yearning, perhaps. Once you have been able to imagine this physical location, relax your 'Gassho hands' onto your lap, with palms no longer touching, only finger tips, your hands resting comfortably on your lap in the midline of your body as you did in our first session together ... if you are sitting in a chair with your feet on the floor, you may wish to allow your large toes to rest against each other. If you are lying down, you could do this also, or you could try placing the soles of your feet flat against each other such that their energy centres are activated and assisting with root chakra energy flow.

Then close your eyes and imagine you are actually present in this imaginary location ... settle in as though you are on retreat in this location ... without any responsibilities ... begin to breathe more slowly and fully ... actually feeling the energy of this place that inspires a feeling of being 'at home' ... relax into this familiar healing energy ... receive its comfort into your being ... allow all your cares to leave your mind as you focus on its peace ... breathe into this feeling of peace and security for several breaths ... ... notice your entire body and mind relaxing into the peacefulness of something more ... welcomed into the comforting arms of familiarity ... of love ... and of a sense of belonging ... This is the grounding and secure energy of your root chakra, mixing with the natural, healing energy of the earth element ... *the energy of something more, in the presence of now* ... remain here for as long as is comfortable for you today.

Reflection

How was this experience for you? You may wish to record any specifics in your journal before moving on in your reading. You may even wish to defer your reading until another time, if you prefer to remain within this healing space awhile longer.

May I also suggest that you go outdoors for a walk at some point today, to physically connect with the earth element. Allow your **Reiki Meditation** experience to replay itself in your mind as you physically connect with the earth and walk in real time. Remember to breathe in your physical experience. See if you can detect 'something more' than you might usually experience while walking outdoors today. If so, please record whatever this might be in your journal when you return home.

Return to your reading only as you are ready.

Welcome back, as you settle in again to your home retreat space! In today's retreat reading, we will look at the first of the five Reiki Precepts and how it applies to your self-care practice.

The Precepts were developed by Reiki's founder, Mikao Usui, to inspire a simple and mindful way of altering behaviours, such that they would be conducive to peaceful living. Somewhat similar to a yoga-inspired Sankalpa, **each of the five Reiki Precepts honours the deeper meaning of life.** In this first precept we are attempting to change the way we approach life, by learning to live without worry, as the precept states: *Just for to day, do not worry.* You might say, **we are learning to be less negative in our thinking and beginning to trust more.**

Worry is one of the most common causes of energy imbalance for many of us. **Worry's stressful energy of anxiety is all-engaging;** it keeps our minds focused on its potential implications. **As we worry, our mind is filled with 'what ifs?'**

Fear is frequently the root cause of our worry. Fear — in the absence of fact — can cause us to invent endless ideas of what might happen concerning the issue or person we are worrying about, keeping us constantly on edge, and uncomfortable. If the tendency to worry has become a habit, such discomfort can lead to increased imbalance. Elevated blood pressure, indigestion, headaches as well as many other symptoms can present as physical and emotional manifestations of worry.

Habitual worry becomes a way of being, a part of what we might call 'lifestyle.' From a personal health perspective alone, therefore, it's important to learn the facts about a situation you are inclined to worry about, *before* investing your time and energy in a fear-filled response. Then you can take concrete action if this is appropriate.

Both fear and worry are forms of energy. So, as well as learning the facts, you can **soothe the way you are feeling by applying your Self-Care Reiki hands to the area in your body that feels your worry.** (We'll come back to this.) This allows Reiki's healing energy to calm your physically experienced anxiety. And perhaps more importantly, Reiki energy will go to your worry's emotional root cause of fear — without your needing to know what this is. Eventually, this energy can be released through a dedicated, daily Self-Care Reiki Meditation practice.

The Reiki precept, *'Just for today, do not worry,'* reminds us to live our life without worry as a way of being. *Can you imagine this?* If worry habitually happens to you, perhaps it is time to ask yourself, *is my worry legitimate?* And as I have said in other publications where worry is discussed, if the answer is 'yes,' then *do* something about it. **Take action!**

If, on the other hand, the answer is 'no,' the Self-Care Reiki precept about worry will help you form a new habit of living your life without worry. To intensify the precept, **turn it into an affirmation in the present tense beginning with the prefix, 'I am' ... such as, 'I am releasing my worry about xxx.'**

So, let's see if we can make this real for you now:

Reflection Exercise

Do you frequently worry about something or someone? Yes? or No? If yes, is this a common worry for you? **If yes, read on ...**

PART ONE

1) First of all, it is necessary to both **acknowledge and feel** the **energy** of your worry and possibly fear ... *in the presence of now* ... and **notice *where* it is located in your body.**

2) Second, **place one or both your hands over the space where you *feel* (and live) this energy of worry ... please do this now.**

3) Ask yourself: *'What am I afraid that might happen?'*

Notice any imagery, thoughts, etc., that come to you as you reflect upon your fear of what might happen ... (Please take the time now to fully immerse yourself in this reflection.)

PART TWO

4) **Feel the warmth of your hand(s) resting on this worry space on your body ... notice how this feels for you ... and take a deep breath into this space beneath your hands.** Continue to keep at least one hand on this place throughout your reading of this chapter. Your physical healing touch will assist your mental and emotional release of worry ... then, repeat the words of the precept about worry to create an affirmation that works for you such as: *I am releasing the energy of worry about xxx from my being.*

5) **The words of your affirmation are meaningful only if you can *feel* the energy of the words.** *Do you believe the words? Or, are you just saying them without engaging in the energy of their meaning?... in the living presence of now? Repeat the affirmation again with feeling ...*

6) **Next, imagine that a positive solution to the problem has been received** and that the source of your worry and fear — *which is in you* — is now surrounded by positive energy flowing beneath your hands ...

7) **Breathe into this positive energy and allow yourself to *actually feel* the energy** of this positive outcome that is for the highest good, **not knowing or needing to know how this has happened.** *By focusing (in the presence of now) on the highest good of the source of your worry, rather than on the worry, you may actually feel a change occurring in your own energy.*

To help you with this, **try to imagine that the problem that has created your worry has already been resolved well beyond your control,** or that the person you commonly worry about is smiling lovingly at you ... **notice how this imagery immediately changes your own energy from one of worry to one of relief.** This is an expansive energy of freedom! **It also liberates the energy of the one for whom you worry.**

To recap:

Your worry has now had the benefit of

- the Reiki precept, as an affirmation *Just for today, I am releasing my worry,*
- gentle hands-on touch to the area of your body that holds worry energy,
- an altered view of what you worry about — seeing the possibility of a positive outcome versus a negative outcome,

* a sense of change in your own energy about your relationship with worry, and

* liberating the subject of your worry from a dysfunctional attachment to you.

* These steps may be enough to release your worry energy from your being.

Should any of this seem confusing, here is a simple example of a common worry that could become habitual — the safety of your family member. As a worrier, you might imagine that his late arrival home from school or work is the result of an accident. If you can manifest such an idea as an accident and all that this might entail, then you can just as easily manifest the idea of seeing him completely safe and on his way home, arriving on time, or perhaps a little late, with a smile on his face, greeting you happily. Obviously, these are two very different energies that create either imagery. **The precept, *Just for today do not worry,* is teaching you to stop worrying as a way of being and living the presence of now!** Instead, place some trust in this person's ability to return home safely. Free him or her from your constant fear of his or her safety! This will be liberating for each of you.

PART THREE

What if my worry continues?

You may wish to draw more directly on the energy of the Universe to partner with you in releasing its root cause, *fear.* So, let's turn our attention now to the Earth Element, as Universal Life Energy, from which roots physically grow. *(Remember that by text-book definition, Reiki is the joining together of Universal Life Force with Vital Life Force. In this case Universal Life Force is the energy of the Earth Element and Vital Life Force is your willingness and intention to heal this part of your life by learning to stop worrying!)*

Healing Self-Care Reiki Meditative Reflection:

Return in your mind to the beautiful location where you initially imagined being on retreat ... feeling very safe and comfortable. I'd like you to take a few moments now, with eyes closed, to draw on the energy that surrounds you in this location, the energy of the earth ...

With your hand still resting against the space in your body where you feel worry:

In your mind and imagination, try to feel the comfort and the connectedness to the healing energy of the Earth Element in this location. Remain mentally focused until you can feel this comfort and connectedness emotionally ... notice how this feels ... in the presence of now! ... *then*

Welcome this grounding and comforting earth energy into the area that is currently holding your worry in your body beneath your warm and comforting hand(s) ... and deeply breathe in its gentle, healing energy ... filling this space of worry in your body, with earth's timeless energy ... in your living presence of now ...

... then flowing out from this space effortlessly, throughout your body and mind ...

... creating gentle healing change within you, supported and grounded by earth's secure energy, positively affirmed through the words, *Just for today, I am releasing worry about xxx ...*

...breathe gently and easily now, completely open to receive the positive stream of Universal Life Energy of the earth as it supports you right now ...

> ... allow a complete release of your worry into the receptive earth where it simply dissolves and disappears ...
>
> Remain in this healing Self-Care Reiki Meditation space for as long as you feel comforted today ...

Afterwards, you may wish to journal your experience and reflect upon this before continuing.

By practicing this technique with any worries you have, you are *releasing yourself from worry as a way of being — of living your presence of now in fear —* **that** *creates* **worry patterns. Worry is contagious.** Its habitual ways are easily passed on to members of families who view life from this fearful way of being. This destructive energy is inhibiting to anyone's personal growth.

A Self-Care Reiki Healing Garden

Another idea for transforming worry as you work with the Universal Life Force of the Earth Element, is to transform your worries into something tangible and beautiful, such as a Self-Care Reiki healing garden.

In this garden, you will plant a new plant or seed, each time you find yourself worrying about something. This will emphasize for you the actual amount of time you are worrying. Then ...

As you transplant each new plant, imagine that you are releasing your specific worry along with its well-established root system of fear into the earth. Remember the phrase, *Just for today I am letting go of worry about xxx ...* as you plant.

Then allow your worries to turn into beautiful blossoms as you learn to live your life without fear and worry.

An alternative to planting a real plant in the soil, is to create a painting in which you paint or sketch a new plant each time a new or chronic worry presents itself, ending with a beautiful painting that reminds you to let go of worry.

The visual of creating a garden of beauty out of release from worry and fear, **is a healing example of working directly with the Universe** ... by feeling (or imagining you can feel) its soft earth receiving your worry plant into its tender care, then carefully dissolving the fear from its roots so that the blossoms of your plant — *aka* YOU — can flourish!

Each day then, the blossoms in your Reiki healing garden, whether real, imagined, or in art form, become your visual reminder that **you are supported by the Universe, by the healing Earth Element; you are supported by the energies of** *all that is.*

Bottom Line Teaching

A Self-Care Reiki practice trains us to live without fear in a 'presence of now' reality by learning to stop worrying as a way of being, setting an example for all with whom we share our life to do the same. As you release the worry habit, you are closer to finding your 'inner home.'

In our next chapter we will look at the precept of living our life in truth. For now, though, please remain in this healing space a little longer, ending with your both hands returning to 'finger tip Gassho' or resting flat and comfortably against your body, with your eyes closed ... enjoying the feeling of positive energy that follows a Self-Care Reiki release ...

Please be gentle with yourself ...

Namaste!

Follow-up thoughts for further reflection:

Worry, is the product of fear. Fear is energy, as is worry. Theoretically, if we can release the energy of fear we can release the energy of worry as well. To carry out the Self-Care Reiki precept, *Just for today, do not worry,* we are not just working with the energy of worry, we are working with its root cause as well ... even though you may not know what this is. You do not have to know! Reiki is energy. Self-Care Reiki, as a healing instrument, works energetically. It is not a psychological process. Therefore, there is no need to spend time analyzing what is at the cause of your worry. If you know that it is a habit, then affirm to stop this habit! However, if its cause is not habit, it may be part of your root chakra energy. It is very appropriate, therefore, to engage the energy of the Earth Element as Universal Life Force to help to heal root chakra issues of energy imbalance. All that's needed is an intention to work with the energy!

Worry usually presents as a thought accompanied by an image of something fearful. To counter worry, is to imagine an alternate thought and image that contains no fear. Such an image contains fear's antithesis, such as peace, joy, love, or light, **presented vividly in your own mental and physical energy awareness.** This is key! **It is one thing to visually *imagine* a change, and another to physically *feel* the change.** Therefore, as we consciously surround the subject of our worry with an imagery containing peace, joy, love or light, as examples, **we connect mentally and physically to these antithetical healing energies** in our imagination, thus displacing our former imagery and consequent energies of fear and worry. **Quite simply, try to replace your worry with the feeling of peace.** This can only work if you know what peace feels like. **If you do not know what peace feels like, then you are holding a book that will teach you how to find out!**

Manifesting Life without Worry

YOGA with Louise Murray

Yoga Posture: Sacred Mountain Pose[17]

The Element: Earth

Chakra: First / Root

Self-Care Reiki Precept:
Just for today, do not worry.

Let us now combine our Self-Care Reiki Practice with the Earth Element, the Root Chakra, and the Yoga Posture of The Sacred Mountain Pose, as we remember the Reiki Precept: *Just for today, do not worry* ... Below Louise's instructions **in plain bold text,** is guided imagery to help you dispel worry as a habit within a simple yoga posture. You may wish to try this outdoors. But first a little background.

The Mountain Pose is the foundation of all standing poses. **In her book, *Yoga Gets Better with Age,*[18] Lilias Folan describes this pose as "Sacred," as in Sacred Mountain Pose, suggesting it acknowledges new beginnings, the present moment, and a sense of returning home to your heart.** *These attributes portray our theme of 'living the presence of now.'* It is, therefore, a beautiful pose to begin our elemental journey of Self-Care

Reiki and Yoga, as I hope you will agree. Please note as well, that this pose can ideally be done outdoors, strengthening the sacred aspect of this pose as you engage in nature with the solid foundation of the earth, in gratitude.

Instructions:

- **Stand tall.**
- **Place the palms of your hands together in front of your chest, feet can be hip-width apart; eyes open and in a soft gaze. Feel your feet connected to the energy of the life-giving earth ... then,**
- **Raise your arms up over your head, in a full stretch with hands facing inwards; relax your shoulders down away from your ears ... then begin to breathe slowly as you relax into this "stately and strengthening posture of The Sacred Mountain."[19]**
- **Visualize roots growing down from your feet deep into the earth providing security against the fear that is at the root of your worry ...**

... slowly breathe healing Earth Elemental Energy of the Universe up through the soles of your feet ... and into your body ...

*... **feel the earth grounding you in a different vision and outcome from that which causes your worry ...** imagine that earth energy is displacing all your fears of worry as it travels throughout your body ... breathe the energy of your new vision up through your body all the way to your finger tips, then releasing your fears into the sky ... where they dissolve into the air ...*

Then bring the palms of your hands together again over your head in a gesture of prayer** as you repeat the words of the precept as affirmation, **I am letting go of worry...

Lower your hands to the front of your chest, palms still together.

***Breathe this new vision throughout your body and mind now like a Salkapa ...** an intention for a new beginning in your relationship with worry ...*

... no longer its victim ... instead, allowing your 'warrior self' to be its conqueror, as you feel your renewed inner strength and power flowing through your body now ...

Pause and give thanks for this healing energy ... the Universal Life Force of the earth pulsating through your body now ... as you bow to the space before you ... and smile your gratitude for this energy change.

NOTE: For all postures in this book, Louise advises the following:

"It's always recommended to use a counter-pose in most cases. I recommend Knee Circles, done lying on the back.

- **As you rest on your back, pull your knees into your chest.**
- **Place one hand on each knee and make circles with your knees together, first clockwise, then counter clockwise.**

Smaller circles massage your lower back close to the spine and larger circles massage outward toward the hips. Experiment to see what feels the best and enjoy your self-massage."

And if you wish to rest awhile longer with your legs stretched out before getting up, you can place your Self-Care Reiki hands comfortably along your hips, the area of your root chakra, then relax into some more self-care time.

Please be gentle with yourself. Namaste!

Energy Wellness Tip

Gratitude Exercise for the Earth Element

Try to walk regularly, several days each week, as a simple and healthy routine to live, walking as much as possible in nature where you can easily connect with the natural elements of Universal Life Energy.

Become aware of the Earth Element beneath your feet as you walk.

Become aware of all of the beauty that surrounds you as you walk in nature ... unplugged ... listening only to natural sounds of birds and breezes, as well as traffic and people ...

Open your awareness to the awesome sky above you ... to the trees around you ... to the grasses or rocks surrounding you ... and whatever other natural gifts that the earth supports in your area.

Breathe in gratitude in your moments of awareness of these environmental gifts and *in the presence of now, give thanks for every living thing.*

If you wish, you can create an affirmation of connection to the Universal Life Energy of these spaces of nature as you walk ... such as

I am connecting to the sky
I am connecting to the trees
I am connecting to the earth
I am connecting to ...
(what you see or hear as you walk)

You can use the Yoga Posture of the Sacred Mountain Pose quite effectively in this healing space.

Feel your energy 'lift' as you increase your level of awareness of your natural surroundings on your walk or Yoga posture, connecting Universal Life Energy with your Vital Life Energy, *aka Reiki!*

CHAPTER THREE

Becoming Authentic ... Living a Life of Truth

A Self-Care Reiki practice trains us to live in a 'presence of now' reality, by living our life in truth in all ways, and finding comfort in our authentic self, the space of our 'inner home.' In this chapter, we look at the realities of living a life that is true to yourself, *or not,* as we speak about our next Reiki precept: *Earn your living honestly,* which we are translating as *Live your life in truth.* We will look to the Universal Life Force of the Water Element — through the metaphor of a stream — to help us learn how the body reacts to living life being true to oneself or untrue. And we will discuss how a Self-Care Reiki lifestyle can consciously and mindfully bring one 'home' to one's true self again. A healing, Self-Care Touch position is described for you as you begin this session. A suggested combination of Self-Care Reiki touch and the Yoga posture of the Supported Bridge will stimulate the Sacral Plexus and Water Element flow in your body to end this session.

To thine own self, be true.[20]

Welcome back! Let's begin our session today with the lighting of your candle, then a moment of pause with your hands in Gassho position ... please acknowledge this moment of awareness of the presence of now that is supported by the light and quiet 'presence' of your candle flame ... slowing things down for you ... before your reading retreat begins. You may wish to create an intention for yourself or to say a short prayer of gratitude for this time you are investing in self care ...

As a quick review, I hope our last session together has increased your awareness of how worry may have been a part of your life to date, and that the session has given you a new road map to begin to eliminate this 'worrisome' habit from your life.

Today, we will be discussing the water element, so before you settle in to your home retreat space ... you may wish to have a glass of water close by to add to your other comforts of candlelight, quiet meditation music and the warmth of a light shawl, should you need it. And, if you enjoyed listening to the sound healing meditation last time, you will find the next in the series for the sacral chakra.[21] Or, perhaps you might enjoy a chant selection from one of my favourite albums, *Beloved*,[22] which speaks to our topic today in a mantra of peace that can be translated as: "Experiencing the Essence of the True Sustainer, the experience of bliss brings into a clear state of awareness." [23] Otherwise, play quiet music that helps you relax, or simply enjoy the silence. And then ...

I would ask you to place your hands on either side of your sacral chakra, in the cradle of your pelvis above your hips, your second chakra ... your sacral chakra ... letting your middle finger tips touch and rest along the centre line of your body.

Assuming you are sitting, rather than lying down, please be aware of your posture also and try to sit tall as you hold this gentle touch position. Then begin to breathe more consciously, for a few breaths, ensuring your inhale and exhale are full and complete, with your exhale a little longer than your inhale. This will expand your lungs and help to rid your body of stale air.

If you prefer to lie down as you use this new Self-Care Reiki gentle touch position, please move into this position now, and just relax completely, eyes closed as you listen to the music or relax into the silence.

We'll begin with using the imagination again to think about a special place in the world that you love where the natural water element is present in any form ... and as you think of this space by the water begin to breathe more slowly and deeply as you focus on the water's presence ... notice the sun shining on the water directly in line with where you are sitting ... breathe in this beauty ... and notice how you feel ... allow yourself to relax even more into this safe and special space by the water for a few more moments, breathing slowly and easily ... noticing the comfort of your hands on your pelvis ... your mind free to completely to relax into this Self-Care Reiki Meditation ... listening to the music or aligning with the silence.

Return to read only when you are ready.

Reflection

How was this for you today? Did you have any images present themselves to you, or thoughts? ... You may wish to take a few moments to capture their memory in your journal.

Continue to hold at least one hand comfortably on the midline of your body over your sacral chakra.

Today, we are speaking about the water element and the Self-Care Reiki spiritual precept that speaks to one's inner truth and freedom to simply be yourself. It goes like this: *Just for today live your life honestly.* **Living honestly, is living your life in truth.**

When you think about living your life in truth, your first thought could be, "Well, I already do this!" The counter question then becomes, *Do you live your truth in all ways?*

To help you consider this, we turn our attention to the water element again and more specifically to the image of a stream, to become aware of its natural flow. If you've been listening to the Sonic Yoga recording, you've heard water sounds ... just connect with or imagine water sounds, and visualize a small stream meandering through a forested area, gurgling as it meets miniature rapids or waterfalls sending up delightful sounds. This version of a stream is simple, true, and *authentic*. The stream is purely a stream with nothing preventing its natural flow.

Now imagine what happens when branches from surrounding trees fall into this small stream. One branch may not make a difference to the swiftness of its water flow. However, over time, if more branches fall into the stream, then its path becomes congested, possibly altering and eventually disrupting its flow. If the debris of the stream is not cleared away, regrettably, the stream's disrupted flow presents as 'normal' to anyone passing by. *Have you ever seen a stream like this?* It is noteworthy that beavers use this principle to purposely disrupt the flow and skilfully create their water homes.

In human terms, the stream is like our human energy system and the water element is like our natural, unimpeded flow of energy throughout our body — our *ki, qi, chi, or prana* — all terms meaning our body's natural and Universal Life Force, or flow of energy in and around the body. Our free-flowing *ki* allows us to feel our life-sustaining zest for life, energy, sustenance and strength. **Like a very young child in our most natural inner state, we embody and reflect the truthfulness of who we are when our internal energy is freely flowing.**

Now, what happens to this natural state if our inner energy flow is interrupted?

It could be said that on a mental / emotional level, anything that slows our internal energy flow and prevents it from sustaining and strengthening us, is not in line with our natural inner truth of who we are. On a physical level, it may represent illness somewhere within the body.

In life, we are constantly making choices. Some of our choices make us feel good and some do not. **Personal growth is not simply about making better choices, it's about noticing how each choice we make affects us** ... this means *noticing how we feel* in our physical, mental or emotional body ... **knowing when to stop doing those things that clearly disrupt or drain our inner flow of energy, or no longer sustain and strengthen us.**

We acknowledge this by *living honestly,* through *the truth of how we feel* as a result of our choice ... *in the presence of now.*

Personal growth is about accepting challenges that will see us move out of our comfort zone to strengthen our inner flow. The dance of life sees us moving in and out of new ideas and ways of living that allow us to acknowledge and strengthen the best parts of ourselves while also maintaining and strengthening our inner flow ... reflecting a sense of, "Yes, this is who I am," back to us through our zest for living ... or, "No, this is not who I am," through how we feel immediately or subsequently, in our emotional, physical and mental bodies as well. **Despite such internal warnings, we may not take heed until much time has gone by, leaving us feeling trapped by a decision taken without acknowledging our inner truth.**

So, where does Reiki come in?

Reiki's energy is always helping us find balance that we might maintain our inner flow, effectively aligned with our inner truth even when obstacles *are* present.

Our Self-Care Reiki practice, as 'present moment energy,' teaches us to become aware, and to acknowledge how we feel at any given time, *in the presence of now*. This means we are more likely to be able to detect an imbalance of "No, this is not who I am," **as it is happening, so as to determine a way to fix it before it gets out of control** ... like the stream, before too many branches impede our natural flow. *Can you relate to this with any experience in your life?*

Having made poor choices, Self-Care Reiki helps us recover ourselves when we are struggling to find our inner truth ... to recover ourselves from the perils of poor choices ... and to heal the effects of those choices. In water element metaphor terminology, Self-Care Reiki helps us begin the removal of the branches that create congestion in our inner stream.

For anyone struggling to figure out who you truly are, a daily Self-Care Reiki practice will help you with this, quite subtly, by allowing you to hear your inner voice and follow it. **These moments of truth can be life changing:**

- Reiki energy is always helping us find, feel and maintain our natural inner flow.

* A complete Self-Care Reiki practice used as daily lifestyle calls us to live our life honestly, by revealing our inner truth in each aspect of our lives.

By adopting a lifestyle of placing your energy-healing Self-Care Reiki hands against your body *every day for a few moments of self care*, you are beginning to bring stillness to your body and mind. **These moments become 'meditation moments.'**

Reiki Meditation energy moments teach you to enjoy 'present moment awareness,' *the living presence of now* ... and therefore, *to become mindful of the times you feel out of balance* — rather like the need to clear branches out of your internal waterway once they have fallen in.

Guided by the Self-Care Reiki Precepts ... especially the one we are discussing at the moment, *I am living my life in truth* ... you are allowing yourself to *be awakened to what your inner truth is, if this has been lost to you.* **You are affirming your authenticity and learning to be guided by your relationship with this energy to follow your inner truth** ... back to the place inside of you that is 'home,' *your authentic self.*

Could a breakdown be the result of a build-up of obstacles?

Sometimes the metaphoric accumulation of branches in your energy system is simply too much debris for the power of the stream to cast off. And some kind of intervention — such as therapeutic counselling — is required to help remove the branches so that the energy can flow again.

Or, sometimes, intervention may be as simple as a need to rest. This is especially true in cases of burnout, where too much is happening in your 24/7 life, regardless of your age. And regardless of stamina and desire, when burnout is pending, it is simply more than you can handle. It may require nothing more than 'time' to step away from some or even all the activity that has led to the burnout or breakdown situation ... time measured in days, weeks, months or even years ... and then one day, with sufficient rest, your inner stream begins to flow again; with renewed strength and vigour, it returns to action.

What does any of this have to do with truth and authenticity?

Let's return to our stream for the answer. The natural free-flowing stream suggests the result of living the life of one's authentic self. Any build up of branches is the result of going against our inherent, natural, inner energy flow, thus departing from our authenticity. One concludes from this example in nature, that the interruption of the stream's natural flow suggests a sluggishness in energy, or a diversion from its natural path, unable to function as well, perhaps even creating a confusion of where it (your life) is going.

What is your truth?

Your truth is the reality of who you really are inside, your authentic self — in stream metaphor terminology, it is your unimpeded connection to the natural direction of energy flow. It has nothing to do with how successful you may perceive yourself to be. **It has everything to do with how you feel at any given time and whether you feel you are being true to yourself in every moment — of being able to answer, "Yes, this is who I am,"** in every action you take along the way, *successful, (whatever this means) or not!*

Truth is tied to your inner happiness and joy. As your inner water element flows freely within you, it leads you to these emotions naturally, as part of your daily life. As a test to whether you are living an authentic lifestyle, therefore, might be to ask yourself this simple question, *Am I happy? (Surely this is the true measure of success!)*

You already know the answer without even needing to stop and consider it!

If your answer *is not* an immediate "Yes," then you might look to the things in your life that are going against your natural flow ... that are creating the build-up of obstacles or branches or diverting your natural path ... separating you from who you truly are in your innermost self. At the same time, ask yourself: *How is my energy level? What is my energy reflecting to me?*

Again, you already know the answers to these questions.

It is so easy to get off track from your authentic self, from who you truly are. If each of your life choices does not honour your authentic self, you may find yourself one day asking yourself: *How did I get here? How did this happen?* And even: *Who am I?*

Beyond any medical or psychological intervention, *is there a role for Reiki?* And the answer is ... a resounding *YES!!* **Reiki as a self-care practice, teaches us to prevent the branches from accumulating in our lives — in our internal waterways. It teaches us to live our life honestly!**

How can Reiki do this?

By virtue of its nature ... going back to our definition from the introduction:

- *Reiki is healing energy,*
- *Reiki is meditation,*
- *Reiki is peace,*
- *Reiki is love and compassion,*
- *Reiki is gratitude,*
- *Reiki is a way of being,*
- *Reiki is mindfulness training,*
- *Reiki is our relationship with ourselves, with one another and with the Universe,*
- *Reiki is an energy that is alive, that heals, that awakens when we open ourselves to it,*
- *Reiki is an energy that guides ... guides us **through** our opening awareness **towards** those things we need, and **away from** those things that may be harmful,*
- *Reiki is life-changing,*
- *Reiki guides us to live in the presence of now.*

A complete Self-Care Reiki practice, used as daily lifestyle always returns us to the presence of now, where our inner truth in each aspect of our lives is revealed, and lived: By adopting a self-care lifestyle of placing your gentle, energy-healing Reiki hands against your body *every day for a few moments ...*

* by *using these self-care moments as meditation,* and

* by *learning to become mindful of the times you feel out of balance,* (guided by the Self-Care Reiki Precepts — especially the one we are discussing at the moment, *I am living my life in truth*)

* by doing these things, you are allowing yourself to *be awakened to what your inner truth is, if this has been lost to you.* You are *affirming your authenticity* and *learning to be guided by* your relationship with this energy to follow your inner truth *in the presence of now* ... back to the place inside of you that is 'home,' the residence of your authentic self, *aka* your 'inner home.'

This is not religion speaking. This is an *internal sense of knowing the difference between what feels right and what does not feel right ...* and *then choosing the obvious.* **This is how those branches can be removed from your natural inner flow of energy and this is how you can prevent more branches from accumulating that may obstruct your natural energy flow.**

As we end our session today, let's come back to an awareness of your hands against your sacral chakra ... add your second hand again for our final meditation to the other side of your body... your inner water element and your second chakra that is the space of creation ... of birth and of re-birth ... and then pause for a moment for you to sense your inner flow of how you feel at this very moment ... then assess truthfully: *how do you feel mentally, emotionally and physically?* ... (Perhaps you may wish to record your observation, afterwards, as evidence to attest to your inner truth.)

And now, direct your breath into the truthfulness of who you truly are even if you aren't certain of what this means — your wholistic self *does* know what this means ... *(just allow yourself to relax and breathe comfortably into this place now, eyes closed, enjoying the warmth and comfort of your hands resting gently on your body, taking all the time you need.)*

The truthful version of who you are is always present in your inner self ... just direct your breath into the natural flow and rhythm of the beautiful energy you truly are ... and repeat these affirming words to yourself ...

- *I am living my life in truth ...*

- *I am living my life in truth ... in this moment, in the presence now*

- *I am living my life in truth ...*

Please continue to hold your hands in place, as you focus on the present-moment reality of your innermost beauty, truth and authenticity ... recognizing that by doing this,

- *you are opening your awareness of yourself as 'something more' than the physical being you see reflected in your mirror ...*

- *you are more than the work or the activities you do ...*

- *you are receiving an invitation from the Universe to live your life from this deeper place within you that **is** your inner truth ...*

- *you are being your authentic and infinite self by accepting the invitation ...*

Please hold these thoughts as you continue to administer self-care touch to your beautiful self today ... remaining here for as long as you need today.

Bottom Line Teaching

A Self-Care Reiki practice trains us to live in a 'presence of now' reality, by living our life in truth in all ways, and finding comfort in our authentic self, the space of our 'inner home.'

In our next session, we'll continue our climb up the energy and elemental ladders to look at the fire element and anger, an obstacle that can create branches in our internal waterways and lead us astray from our authentic selves. Until then, please remember to be gentle and true to yourself *in all ways.* Namaste!

Becoming Authentic ... Living a Life of Truth

YOGA with Louise Murray

Yoga Posture: Supported Bridge, with block, elevating the Sacrum

The Element: Water

Chakra: Second / Sacral Plexus

Self-Care Reiki Precept:
Earn your living honestly / Live your life in truth.

This combination of element, exercise and energies is offered to restore a sense of internal security and wholeness.

Instructions:

- **For this pose you will need a yoga block or a firm cushion close to you.**
- **Lie down with your knees bent and the soles of your feet on the floor about hip width apart.**
- **As you press on your feet, lift your hips and place the prop under your sacrum (the flat part of your lower back).**
- **Roll your shoulders under.**

Once comfortably in place, lay your Self-Care Reiki hands on either side of your pelvis as you have earlier in this chapter, with your fingers pointing inwards towards your midline. Make sure your elbows are comfortable in this position; your hands may be more comfortable if resting in an upwards V formation against your pelvis.

Repeat the Affirmation: *I am living my life in truth,* as mantra, as you relax into the posture ... then if you wish ...

Visualize the Universal energy of the Water Element flowing out from this life-giving sacral plexus region of your body ... feel the support beneath your sacrum, representing the freedom you have to express your own truth about who you are and who you are becoming in this moment of life-affirming breath you are breathing ...

... feel the connection you are making with your truth, in the presence of now ...

... rest into this awareness ...

... ***birth and breathe this awareness of your self into your outer world*** *in this present moment of now ... affirming: I am living my life in truth!*

... ***feeling fully alive, thriving*** *... as your affirming breath of life receives its entitled energy from the Universe to breathe freely ... in ... and out ...* ***restoring you with your inherent energy of your truth ...***

... imagine that your inner Water Element is carrying your truth throughout your body, entering every cell of your being, ***liberating***

you to heights of awareness of your beautiful self you have not known before ...

... with full appreciation for who you are in *this* moment ... **feel the presence of now in this reality of who you are** ... and who you always will be ... *the real you ...*

Louise:

To release the pose: Press on your feet, lift your hips, remove the prop, and slowly lower your body to the floor ...

... then feel the firm support of the floor beneath your sacrum ... bend your knees and place your feet flat against the floor ... adjust your warm Self-Care Reiki hands to comfortably rest against your lower abdomen ... in gratitude ... as this energy continues to flow freely throughout your body.

Stretch your legs out fully next, with your hands still in place.

* *

NOTE: For all postures in this book, Louise advises the following:

"It's always recommended to use a counter-pose in most cases. I recommend Knee Circles. *(Please refer to photo on page 45.)*

* **As you rest on your back, pull your knees into your chest.**
* **Place one hand on each knee and make circles with your knees together, first clockwise, then counter clockwise.**

Smaller circles massage your lower back close to the spine and larger circles massage outward toward the hips. Experiment to see what feels the best and enjoy your self-massage."

Then rest here awhile longer, in deserved enjoyment of your gentle Self-Care Reiki bath of security and wholeness, acknowledging your inner truth. Before getting up, turn over onto one side, rest a moment, then sit up, eyes still closed, with hands in front of your chest, acknowledging gratitude for the feeling of peace flowing in your body, with a smile on your face.

Please be gentle with yourself. Namaste!

Energy Wellness Tip

Gratitude Exercise for the Water Element

Try to increase your daily intake of natural water in your diet, and in between meals as part of a healthy routine. As you sip your water, be conscious of the distance it has travelled before you were able to open a tap to drink it. Notice its clarity as you drink ... and give thanks for your ability to consume it so freely, recognizing that in many parts of the world, clean and accessible drinking water is not possible.

Breathe in gratitude in your moments of awareness of these things and *in the presence of now, give thanks for every living thing.*

CHAPTER FOUR

Anger as an Obstacle to Peace

Do you live with someone who seems angry all the time? Or do you find yourself rising to angry reactions easily?

A Self-Care Reiki practice trains us to live in a 'presence of now' reality, as we release the energy of anger from our being and uncover the peace that lives within the warmth of our 'inner home' space. In this chapter, anger is introduced as an obstacle to living an authentic life and finding inner peace *in the presence of now.* Mikao Usui, Reiki's founder, set the goal of Anshin Ritsumei, a Japanese term meaning 'peace within chaos,' as a meaningful result of a Reiki practice and lifestyle. The Self-Care Reiki precept: 'Just for today, do not anger,' teams up with the Universal Life Force of the Fire Element to make us aware of anger's impact on our Solar Plexus energy. Self-Care Reiki guides us to live without anger and create a more balanced reaction to life's challenges and opportunities. A gentle Self-Care Reiki Touch position on your body affected by anger will help to restore a sense of calm. Ending our retreat chapter is the Yoga posture of a seated forward bend, also known as 'The Caterpillar.' This posture stimulates Solar Plexus and Fire Element flow within the body.

I am in you and you are in me!
Together we engage in this journey.
Together, we teach each other,
Reflect each other's
Imperfections and perfections
As we strive for harmony
As we try to remember that
We are in all that is.

Hello again and welcome back. I hope you are continuing to affirm your authenticity through the precept, *I am living my life in truth*. This precept, as with all of the Reiki teaching is about lifestyle. That said, try to become aware and observant of times when you are not considering your own truth in decisions you are making, however trivial they may seem. When you catch yourself during one of these times, stop and consider correcting your approach in that presence of now moment ... then, **notice how you feel afterwards. It is precisely moments like these, where you connect with Source energy that allows peace and love to enter.** And as you will see in today's reading, *this is the secret in letting go of anger also.*

In this session, we will be discussing our third Self-Care Reiki precept and the Fire Element, as we introduce an obstacle in living our truth, anger. Suggested music from Insight Timer for today's Reiki Meditation accompaniment, is Deep Peace Guitar,[24] a peaceful accompaniment to your meditation shortly.

As you light your candle today, please pause again in Gassho position, to create an intention for yourself. If anger has been an issue for you, may you find something within today's text that will offer solace to your being. Open to the 'presence of now awareness' of this magical moment as your candle takes on light and shares its peace with you ... acknowledge your gratitude for this 'magical moment' as you take a few slower breaths to breathe in this warm sensation of light and peace ... this will help to stimulate your flow of third chakra energy in your body, connecting you with the warmth and beauty of the Fire Element as Universal Life Energy.

In today's Self-Care Reiki gentle touch position, please rest your hands comfortably against your solar plexus, the space beneath your rib cage and just above your navel. Relax your hands as your finger tips touch in the midline of your body. You may wish to lie down to do this or sit up with your back straight, or relax in a chair with your feet up, prepared to close your eyes and enjoy the full benefits of this position for as long as you feel content within it.

Your hands are now resting on the home of your inner sun, your inner Fire Element. Feel the gentle warmth from your hands as you settle in ... slowing your breath ... resting into the peaceful music ... breathing more consciously ... filling your lungs on your in-breath, then fully exhaling ... taking a few breaths this way, until you feel your body completely relaxing ... then relax your breath and feel your mind slowing and centering.

When you are ready to return to reading, try to continue to hold one hand in place on your solar plexus as you use the other to support your book or tablet.

Reflection

Did you have any thoughts arise during this time of relaxation that are related to today's topic? You may wish to record these in your journal before continuing.

When Reiki's founder, Mikao Usui, created the precept: *Just for today, do not anger* as part of his Reiki teachings, he was attempting to bring more peace into the lives of those who were the recipients of his treatments and teachings. His ultimate goal was to help people develop Anshin Ritsumei, a Japanese word meaning 'peace amidst chaos.' Letting go of anger is a good place to start to accomplish this.

Whereas anger can inspire such positive change in society as creating social justice out of injustice — as witnessed at the time of this writing, through people all over the world protesting systemic racism — living the reality of unwanted anger as a daily habit is stifling to positive mental and emotional growth and wellbeing. Anger detracts from a peaceful way of being and as a follow-through from our last session, it leads us away from our authentic self.

Anger is a powerful energy that creates upheaval in its recipients as well as its instigators. **Memories of anger can remain throughout a lifetime stored within the energy of our emotions,** possibly serving as a deterrent from feeling the freedom of one's authentic self. Anger prevents a lifestyle of truth, when one submits to the negative energies of its demands.

Let's look at anger energy close up: I would like you to think about a time when someone has been angry with you or angry with someone close to you while you were present to witness an angry exchange ... or, in the unusual event that this may never have happened, *has there been a time in your life when you have become angry with someone or some thing?*

As you recall a time(s) when you have been exposed to one side of anger or the other ... **notice where in your body you are feeling your memory,** as we did with worry. Because, *yes,* very definitely *we feel the energy of* anger in our body as well as in our mind (through our memories.) If you have been a victim of anger in your early life, or at *any* time in your life, *or even now* ... you know this to be true.

Reiki energy is always going to the source of one's discontent and dredging up the harmful energies to be looked at and released.

Now, notice where your hand has been resting ... *is it centred on the space that holds any anger you have experienced in your lifetime?* If not, then move it to where you do feel anger. Often, this space is centered in the solar plexus; however, **intense**

anger can impact each of our core energy centres and higher, thwarting normal energy flow in these centres — like a build-up of branches, creating an obstruction in our internal waterway we discussed last time. **This has ramifications for one's ability to feel a sense of peace;** influenced instead, perhaps, by the energy of fear — fear of anger erupting at any time. **It is important, therefore, to speak about anger as a disruptive energy force in one's life.**

When I speak about the Fire Element, I like to suggest that we all have what is like a pilot light burning inside of us in our third chakra. And as pilot lights are intended, they burn calmly with a balanced glow of inner light, prepared to flare up with the correct stimulus. So, for example, when you are being creative with free-flowing water elemental energy and second chakra inspiration, your fire elemental energy and third chakra are stimulated and energized to carry out your plan or project. **This is a more positive example of how our energy system is connected and works together.**

Let's look at what happens to our inner pilot light when anger is present. If someone is angry with you, you may retaliate with anger of your own — thus causing your pilot light to flare up, possibly out of control. Conversely, as witness to an angry exchange directly or indirectly, you may react in a way in which the one who is angry almost blows out your pilot light, rendering you helpless to react.

The Self-Care Reiki precept, *Just for today, do not anger,* was created to prevent this stifling, almost paralytic reaction from happening; it teaches us to prevent anger from having any part in our life. It places us on a life path of dealing with our life in new and mindful ways that do not involve the need to get angry, or to remain in the presence of one who is chronically angry or easily susceptible to angry outbursts.

If you have been traumatized by anger in your life, this destructive energy may need a boost to help move it out of your being through physical movement such as as running, speed-walking, swimming laps, bicycling or lifting weights. The precept can be used as an affirmation: *I am letting go of anger about xxx,* spoken out loud in rhythm with your body movements.

In severe emotional trauma caused by anger, counselling with a family therapist may also be essential to allow you to speak about its affects on you during your lifetime. Discussing issues of anger-related trauma brings full acknowledgement to what you have been holding, allowing for release through your speaking of it.

Self-Care Reiki partners very well with therapeutic counselling and Yoga to help anyone go through this kind of release journey in their lives. Yoga postures stimulate meridian flow along the body that holds this energy. Gentle hands-on touch against the energy centres where you specifically feel the memory of anger both comforts and stimulates release. **These three therapies combine beautifully, to help release anger energy, and restore mental and emotional health and wellbeing.**

It is important to understand that each memory we have contains an energy that can warm us as we remember, elevating our energy; or, memories can create the opposite effect energetically. Energies that elevate us, nourish our life force, by stimulating our *ki energy*. Energies that bring us down, drain our life force, or *ki energy*. **The good news is that because our memories contain energy we can, with time, release this negative and draining anger energy from our being.** We cannot remove the memory; however, we *can* remove its energy hold over us. This point is worthy of your consideration if you have been victim to anger.

Reiki energy is always going to the source of one's discontent and dredging up harmful energies to be looked at and released. The memory of words is another example of this.

Words are powerful and cannot be taken back after being said by one who is out of control with anger, possibly affecting their receiver for a lifetime. Even in old age, the memory of a parent's scolding words can still insight the same self-destructive energy as they did in childhood, decades earlier, as such thoughts emerge in later years. If you have been affected by destructive words during your life, then all of the preceding discussion on anger is important for you as well.

Words are equally powerful when used to show compassion and understanding. Even one kind word and gesture can make a difference to one's day and to one's life. **Kind words during a difficult encounter of anger, rather than an angry response, are like a life-raft being thrown to one who is drowning in his own unease.** Living the precept, *Just for today, do not anger,* one day at a time, is important in all areas of life and **especially during child rearing, and interactive behaviours with family members.**

Third chakra and Fire Element energies have the capacity to be warm and hospitable with others. An example of third chakra imagery is sharing the warmth of a fireside chat or a kitchen table that is surrounded by the kindness of family or friends, and filled with good food ready to delight, nourish and sustain. These are all healing energies supplied by third chakra warmth and fire elemental awareness and intention. Meeting for coffee with a friend is an example of this also. *Can you imagine how anger could completely disrupt warm and comforting scenes?*

So from a simply human perspective let me repeat a couple of verses from our poem, that speaks to the interconnectedness we have with one another and with all that is ... and how w*hat we do to one, is felt by others!*

We are in all that is
We are each a part of the Universe
We are in our friends and in our enemies
We are in all that is.
I am in you and you are in me!
Together we engage in this journey.
Together, we teach each other,
Reflect each other's
Imperfections and perfections
As we strive for harmony
As we try to remember that
We are in all that is.

The precept, *Just for today do not anger,* is teaching us to not provoke, intimidate or retaliate with unkindness; instead, it encourages us to try to restore peace by finding harmonious ways of handling difficult situations.

From a hands-on perspective, **Self-Care Reiki Meditation seeks balance,** and when practised regularly, Reiki energy subtly begins to create a sense of peace within the body and mind, **while moving us further away from negative emotions such as anger.**

Such change *within us,* begins to distance us from those in our life who embody angry energy. By separating ourselves from their influence in our life, we can begin to heal the truth of our pain we have experienced from anger's powerful influence ... from anger's harmful energy ... opening us to experience and live the presence of now in positive ways that promote our personal growth and wellbeing.

The key in all of this, therefore, is the need to remove oneself from the destructive energy of anger and the overwhelmingly stifling environment it creates, overtaking its victims's lives ... with its power to destroy confidence, self-esteem, hope and faith in something more. ***This is a state of spiritual distress!***

I implore anyone resonating with these words to have a good look in your own mirror ... and honestly ask yourself if you are victim of another's anger ...and if so, to seek help, safely ...

Do you remember the words from our first session together, where we spoke about Self-Care Reiki energy connecting us with our 'inner Universe' and uniting us with the living and infinite aspects of ourselves we've not known before, or perhaps have forgotten?

Connected to this inner Universe, or *ki energy,* is our 'outer Universe,' *or Rei energy.* This is the infinite part of ourselves that contains the healing elemental energies found throughout the Universe ... **a key aspect of *our* awakening therefore, *of our presence of now,* is a conscious awareness of this *complete Universe* we embody within us** ... *the unification of Universal Life Force and Vital Life Force, also known as Reiki!*

When our Vital Life Force is chronically stifled with something such as anger or suppression, our Reiki potential is stifled also and cannot flourish! In Fire Element terms, our pilot light is almost burned out! Instead of growing into the fullness of our human potential, we are deprived of knowing who we truly are. We are disconnected from ourselves in such moments. This is traumatic and life-changing!

Is there a way out of this disconnect with oneself?

Yes! (Remembering that we are energy, and that all of life has energy!)

There is a way out of this energy disconnect ... by first removing ourselves from all influence of suppression, then by beginning the restorative process of rebalancing our energy in ways that are being shared in this book. Anger is not the only cause of disconnect. Being overburdened by any of life's unfair and unjust demands, as, for example in the workplace, can also create such an end result.

Finding the sense of re-connection with the part of us that is lost when we suffer from abuse of any form, **is like coming back home to oneself.** It is the wordless response I see in clients who simply cannot describe how they feel following a Reiki session on the table. The forgotten sensation of consciousness — *pure consciousness of connection with oneself* — is so foreign as to feel unreal, and yet completely comforting at the same time.

Preventing Dis-connection

As we discussed in the last retreat chapter, making conscious choices based on how you feel in the presence of now is about remaining connected with your true self. This remains one of your greatest sources of prevention from dis-connect. However, to do this may take time to understand within your own being.

When we are consciously aware of our internal connection with Reiki, we experience *the presence of now* ... the healing space within us that *feels complete* and right within us. This is our place of inner truth, where energies of anger and worry do not exist.

When our thoughts are filled with negative emotions and memories of worry and anger and fear, jealousy, resentment, and so forth, we are dis-connected with our truth. **And yet, this inner healing space of *connectedness constantly resides within us all the time ... always ready to move into our daily life as we acknowledge its presence.*** Reiki is a vehicle to make this happen!

I do not want to leave you with the impression that Reiki is the only energy-healing modality that can be helpful for victims of abuse. What I do wish to highlight, is that it is a simple modality that can be used on oneself! As well, Reiki does not interfere with medical treatment, nor is it a replacement for medical treatment. Reiki is considered 'complementary therapy,' not alternative therapy ... complementing and supporting other therapies, as opposed to taking the place of other therapies.

Underlying Self-Care Reiki, is the use of our gentle hands-on touch. Practiced daily, **Reiki energy quite naturally flows to those areas of imbalance, affected by anger and other destructive energies, restoring harmony, whether or not we use the Reiki precept.** And this is important! When one suffers trauma, such as the effects of anger, the suggestion of using an affirmation may require more mental energy than you currently have ... especially when this book is suggesting five Precepts to use!

Once again, here is good news. As long as you rest your own hands upon your body anywhere — *yes, anywhere* — with an intention for Reiki energy to flow, you are receiving the benefit of this healing resource even within your mental exhaustion. Just close your eyes and breathe in its soothing comfort. *(You may not even require an attunement to Reiki to experience this!)*

With Reiki, energy is always moving to restore and stabilize. As we place our hands gently upon our body, the energy naturally flows towards the areas of our body and mind that are out of balance. It is beyond our control. *Look upon it as Source energy moving in to comfort you, 'holding you' in your time of need.*

By adding the Precepts in conjunction with gentle hands-on touch, we are training ourselves to become consciously aware of harmful energies of such things as worry and anger ... and move towards becoming more compassionate with ourselves and with others, the subject of our next reading retreat chapter.

As we close out our session today, notice how this reading has affected you and where in your body you may have felt emotion. By reflecting upon this, you are heightening your conscious awareness of harmful energies of anger you may (still) hold within your body and mind if this has been an issue for you ...

Breathe into this space now ... with your hand(s) still in place, perhaps allowing the water element to help you with this through the release of long held tears if this comes naturally to you ... as you acknowledge the harm that the energy of anger has caused you during your life, or someone else who may have been the recipient of *your* anger ...

Tears can be a powerful release when energies have been held for extended periods. And as we remember the metaphor of the stream from our last session, your tears may serve to remove the obstacles in your inner water element's energy, allowing normal energy flow to return again.

As you continue to engage in this gentle Self-Care Reiki touch exercise, please be gentle with yourself, taking all the time you need ... and remember the words from the poem:

I am in you and you are in me!
Together we engage in this journey.
Together, we teach each other,
Reflect each other's
Imperfections and perfections
As we strive for harmony
As we try to remember that
We are in all that is.

Bottom Line Teaching

A Self-Care Reiki practice trains us to live in a 'presence of now' reality, as we release the energy of anger from our being and uncover the peace that lives within the warmth of our 'inner home' space.

Until next time: *I bow to the Divine in you* ... I see only the beautiful parts of you that hold your deepest blessings of who you truly are and the many gifts you have to offer to the world. ***May you see them also!*** Please be gentle with yourself! Namaste!

Anger as an Obstacle to Peace

YOGA with Louise Murray

Yoga Posture: The Caterpillar (seated forward bend)

The Element: Fire

Chakra: Third / Solar Plexus

Self-Care Reiki Precept:
Just for today, do not anger.

The Caterpillar, or seated forward bend, is an excellent daily posture to stimulate energy flow and assist with digestion, set within the solar plexus, and influenced by the Fire Element.

Instructions:

Many people benefit from using a cushion or folded blanket under their buttocks to help keep a healthy sacral tilt. Also, if your hamstrings are tight, it's fine to bend your knees slightly.

* **Start in a seated position with your legs extended. Keeping your back straight, inhale, and as you exhale, slowly bend forward moving from the hips until you can't go any farther. Then, if it's comfortable for you, let your back relax into a soft curve using a gentle touch on your legs as your body folds onto itself, like a caterpillar.**

* **Don't strive to go deeper. Just breathe, relax, and enjoy being just where you are.**

Once you have reached a point where you can remain in this inner yin yoga posture of relaxation and restoration, remember your mantra, *I am letting go of anger,* using your mind to bring your awareness to the space in your body where you may feel anger ... then,

... visualize your Fire Element as your inner pilot light ... your gentle, steady inner presence of light that is always ready to be your inner sense of knowing ... your inner guide, never burning out of control ... restoring your inner harmony and balance ...

... as you breathe this healing thought throughout your body now ... hold the position as long as is comfortable for you up to two — four minutes, knowing your conscious awareness has experienced the intention of your mantra in the presence of now ...

... then begin to raise your body back up again slowly, vertebrae by vertebrae ... until your upper body is completely upright ... eyes remaining closed ...

... then slowly lie down on your back and allow your body to stretch out fully, hands above your head ...

... then bring your Self-Care Reiki hands to your solar plexus region directly beneath your rib cage, resting your palms on either side of your body comfortably, and breathe slowly, for a few moments of peaceful relaxation ...

⊛ ⊛ ⊛ ⊛ ⊛ ⊛ ⊛ ⊛ ⊛ ⊛ ⊛ ⊛ ⊛ ⊛ ⊛ ⊛ ⊛ ⊛ ⊛ ⊛

NOTE: For all postures in this book, Louise advises the following:

"It's always recommended to use a counter-pose in most cases. I recommend Knee Circles. *(Please refer to photo on page 45.)*

* **As you rest on your back, pull your knees into your chest.**
* **Place one hand on each knee and make circles with your knees together, first clockwise, then counter clockwise.**

Smaller circles massage your lower back close to the spine and larger circles massage outward toward the hips. Experiment to see what feels the best and enjoy your self-massage."

... then turn over on your side, rest for a moment, then slowly sit up again, a smile on your lips ... then bring your hands together

in front of your chest in gratitude for the comfort of knowing that you have welcomed healing energy into your life today, to calm the eruption of outbursts of anger or the effect upon you of such memories ...

... with eyes still closed and hands still in place in front of your chest, in Gassho, welcome peace into all the spaces where anger has lived ... Anshin Ritsumei ... the ability to find peace within chaos, regardless of what happens around you ...

Please be gentle with your beautiful self ... Namaste!

Energy Wellness Tip

Gratitude Exercise for the Fire Element

One way of experiencing the warmth of the fire element is to connect with a friend or relative by telephone or a visit, rather than by text or email. As you hear the 'live' and familiar voice of this person, or see him or her in person over coffee or other enjoyable visit, acknowledge your thanks 'in the presence of now' for this connection, and notice how your attention to gratitude makes you feel inside. Recognize that your friend is likely feeling this way also. Also notice how you feel when you say goodbye.

CHAPTER FIVE

Show Compassion to Yourself and Others

A Self-Care Reiki practice trains us to live in a 'presence of now' reality, finding love and compassion in our relationship with ourself as well as others, using forgiveness as a form of release ... recognizing that these are the qualities of our 'inner home' heart space of truth and peace.

In this chapter, we combine 'Ki' Heart Chakra energy with 'Rei' Universal Life Force (*energy*) of the Air Element as we administer Self-Care Reiki. *(Translation: as we place our self-care hands gently on our heart centre, we use the breath to help us feel compassionate towards ourself and others.)*

Added to this is the fourth Reiki precept, 'Show compassion to oneself and to others,' adapted from the original, which stated: 'Honour your parents, teachers and elders.' The modern adaptation addresses the fundamental need to honour the self as well. The use of the more globally understood term, 'compassion,' suggests a more conciliatory attempt to understand and possibly forgive, as opposed to 'honour.' **The healing effect of these three factors of touch, the breath and a mindful precept working together, is the potential ability to release harmful energies such as anger that we discussed in the last chapter.** Compassion opens our heart centre, allowing us to both love and become compassionate towards the needs of others as well as ourselves. A healing, heart-centred Self-Care Reiki touch position combines with the Air Element in a Yoga Heart-Centre opening posture to end this session.

Photo by Drew Campbell

We carry the possibility of the sacred within us at all times allowing us to see the best in others and in ourselves within the sacred space that surrounds us. [25]

Hello again! To prepare for today's heart-centred retreat, you may wish to play the sound healing music of the Heart Chakra Tibetan Singing Bowls,[26] or perhaps something else you prefer which is peaceful for you; then light your candle in your retreat space. Again, please take a moment with your hands in Gassho position to acknowledge the beginning of our time together today and your intention for this time you are spending in self care.

Once settled, let's begin immediately to show compassion to yourself by placing your hands gently upon the centre of your chest, your heart centre, or fourth chakra. This is particularly important if anger has been a part of your life, as we discussed last time.

First, though, a word of clarification. Feeling compassion for yourself does not mean feeling sorry for yourself! Rather, it is looking at yourself through a lens of love rather than criticism. Many of us dislike ourselves and find fault with ourselves on a daily basis, feeling as though we do not measure up to some immeasurable and imaginary judgement call. Consequently, it is easy to begin to feel sorry for ourselves. This is not an energy of healing. It is an energy of wanting to get even, of dislike, or of anger, perhaps.

A second discerning clarification concerning compassion is the separation of ego and spirit. When we expect something to happen 'our way' and it does not, it is easy to fall into an egocentric view of the situation placing blame or anger on another or doubt upon oneself. In these views, compassion is absent. In moments such as this, compassion is needed to dissolve blame, anger or doubt. In compassion, the situation is viewed through the lens of trust in oneself, removing all expectations of outcome. This is another form of self love, loving oneself enough to trust in oneself, and one's own actions. In compassion, we surrender the outcome to 'the Universe.' This is a huge lesson in trusting others as well as oneself, and is fundamental in our understanding the breadth of discussion possible concerning compassion and its intertwined relationship to forgiveness, acceptance and love.

When we speak of compassion, we are learning to look at ourselves, not as victim (ego); rather, as a beautiful spirit trying to live life each day loving and accepting who he or she is and is becoming. We win some and we lose some. What is important is we try, and continue to keep trying. It _will_ become easier!

If you are sitting up, you may wish to place one hand over the other in the centre of your chest. If you are lying down, it is easier to place your hands against the outer walls of your chest on either side of your body, fingers pointed inwards towards the centre of your chest, making sure your arms and hands are relaxed in either of these positions. Relax into your own gentle self-care touch ... and then, begin to breathe with awareness of the position you are holding and why ... breathing slowly and completely into the concept of being compassionate with yourself. Remain in this position for as long as is comfortable for you before reading further. Relax into the healing sounds of music, and allow your mind to focus on compassion as it relates to you ... Perhaps the following words will help you to focus compassion, if this is new to you:

We carry the possibility of the sacred within us at all times allowing us to see the best in others and in ourselves within the sacred space that surrounds us. [27]

Reflection

Self-Care Reiki touch and breathing compassion for oneself will fill an empty soul and feed oneself with love.

Have your gentle hands-on touch and thoughts of self-compassion filled you up?

Do you feel like your soul has been fed with love?

Please rest into this reflection for awhile before reading on. Perhaps you may wish to journal any thoughts that are coming to you.

Let's work with this last question.

Are you able to sense the energy of love and compassion flowing or beginning to flow within you, in the presence of now? The star in all of this, of course, is the breath, breathing oxygen from the Air Element, picked up by the bloodstream, engaging the Water Element.

This is one of life's amazing miracles that we simply take for granted. Your inner Universe of Water and Air Elements work together all the time to make this happen as we breathe. By adding Self-Care Reiki gentle touch and by mindfully adding the Reiki precept, in the form of an affirmation — *I am showing compassion to myself (and others)* — you are consciously adding the energy of compassion to the mix of Self-Care Reiki energy already flowing within you.

By practicing Self-Care Reiki in this very mindful way, in the presence of now, you 'open' mentally, emotionally and physically to the broader topic of holistic compassion for yourself as well as for others. Energetically, your heart chakra responds by opening in sync with the changes in your mental, emotional and physical reactions.

Think back to our last session when we spoke about anger ... you can more easily appreciate how the ability to take slower and deeper breaths in the midst of an episode of anger, will allow you to find that deep, centred and quiet space inside of you where peace resides, despite the chaos of your outer environment. This is the self-care healing space of Anshin Ritsumei that Reiki's founder, Mikao Usui, described as the ultimate goal of a Reiki practice.

Within this inner space of peace, or Anshin Ritsumeu, lies the loving heart energy that is within us all ... the healing space that breeds compassion for others as well as ourselves. So, rather than react to another's angry outburst with a venom of our own, instead, we learn to react with compassion. (And it may require several deep breaths or a silent counting to ten, or higher, to do this.)

A tender reaction (by you) from a compassionate heart, can extinguish your raging fire of anger energy as simply as if you were blowing out a candle flame! The consequent, compassionate feeling restores your inner pilot light to a controlled, warm comfort level again as the source of your anger energy has been neutralized.

Reflection Moment ... please reflect upon this last paragraph and then consider the following questions as you journal your thoughts.

- *Can you imagine doing this?*
- *Can you imagine reacting with compassion to another's anger rather than with anger yourself?*
- *Can you imagine being on the receiving end of a compassionate response when you are upset with anger ... and how this would feel?*

A fully functioning first, second and third chakra automatically support a fully functioning heart chakra. *What do I mean by this?*

Imagine you are building a house, such as you see on the HGTV network, or a house being built in your own neighbourhood. The foundation is always the first step. And it must be perfect to withstand the load that will be built upon it. **In energy-healing terms, your root chakra needs to be cleared of all imbalance for it to support the load of the energies of a lifetime you will experience.**

And then as the house begins to take shape, it requires plumbing — with perfect hook-ups — or there will be issues 'downstream' for you as home owner; such issues must be resolved if there's faulty plumbing. Of course, we are speaking of second chakra energy and the Water Element. **Faulty construction (debris) cannot be present in your internal waterway, or you will have problems supporting your energy centres higher up, such as your third or fourth chakra. So your internal Water Element must be freely flowing.**

If you live in cooler climates, you will need a heating system, equivalent to your third chakra energy, or Fire Element. This must be installed properly or there will be defections that could actually be quite unsafe in your new home. And certainly, defections or **imbalances of third chakra energy will not be able to support your heart center's need to offer warmth and support to yourself or to others.**

Open, heart-centered energy is essential to support you. It is also essential to allow you to support others!

Self-Care Reiki is rather like becoming a repair person *to resolve issues with your foundation, your water works or your heating system of your internal home so that you can live there safely and happily.*

When you function like the well-built house, with all amenities working in rhythm and harmony, your energy is able to serve you like a beautiful temple, a fortress and a comforting retreat. At the same time, you can stand tall within your community, giving purpose, pleasure and meaning to your life.

The Self-Care Reiki journey is actually a journey of release, of loving repair and healing, such that we can truly understand what it means to be compassionate towards ourselves as well as towards others ... *we can truly say that we love ourselves and that we love our life ... despite what happens along the way.*

As you engage in your own Self-Care Reiki journey, not all days will be filled with the magical colour, beauty and fragrance, for example, of wisteria growing in the garden of your well-built home. In fact, some days can bring up the darkness of stinky old roots (of root chakra energy) that have been masked during a lifetime of covering up or pretending they aren't there, rotting away ... Or your garden may reveal a stagnant swamp (of sacral chakra energy) that now attracts mosquitos that sting and itch ... Or, your garden could reveal once beautiful plantings burned to a crisp by the heat of the sun, (of solar plexus energy) ... As you focus on a Self-Care Reiki daily practice of healing, these metaphoric stinky roots, stagnation or burned-out plantings will come to the surface for release — each having its own energy, its own Vital Life Force that has been compromised!

These are the healing days of release, when Self-Care Reiki compassion towards yourself and others is so important. And coincidentally, these are the days when the Universal Life Force of the Earth, Water and Fire elemental energies can be healing partners for you in your Self-Care Reiki practice.

So what we're saying is, each of the core chakra energies needs to be free flowing to support the fourth chakra of heart-centred energy; it is from this energy that we live most of our life in relationship with ourselves and with others. **We cannot live compassionately with ourselves if we are holding on to issues of the past that are preventing free-flowing energy in our core chakras.** *(We cannot live compassionately with ourselves when we still have stinky old roots rotting in our garden, etc.)*

Nature can be an untapped source of healing for you as you exercise the affirmation of letting go of destructive energy. As you raise energies of the past and acknowledge their source of your imbalance, take yourself into nature where you are surrounded by the elements that support this imbalance quite naturally.

Then breathe in the energy of the air element and imagine it going directly to the source of your imbalance. Sit down in nature with your hands resting on your body where you feel the most inner distress. Breathe into this space gently, in the presence of now, as you remember the affirmation:

* *I am showing compassion to myself, or*
* *I am healing myself with love and compassion.*

Healing is a process; your daily Self-Care Reiki practice supports this process.

As you remember to be compassionate with yourself and with those who may have hurt you in the past, Self-Care Reiki will support you within your healing process. As you will see below, **compassion is linked to release and forgiveness, in an ever-revolving flow of these energies: release, compassion and forgiveness.**

Without *the presence of now* **showing up in any one of these energies, it is unlikely that either of the other two energies will support your inner truth!** In other words, forgiveness must be a conscious process — in the presence of now — flowing from compassion, to be able to release the energy of the transgression that has affected you. One cannot simply give 'lip service' to words of forgiveness. Forgiveness must be real. It must contain the energy of love and compassion.

It is your heart that knows your inner truth, your energy of love and peace. *Your heart centre can only be reached and engaged through the energies of love and compassion for yourself and for others. Otherwise, forgiveness is impossible. And therefore, release is impossible.*

So pull out those stinky old roots! ... *They have been rotting away inside of you breeding anger or depression, or jealousy, etc., instead of love and compassion. This creates imbalance all along the way in your core energies, and threatens to crumble the walls of your well-built house!*

Release is like a dance of energy opening in any of the centres inviting other centres to join in the dance. Sometimes the dance is one that requires further awareness and reflection before that invitation can be accepted.

Release and compassion are intertwined, needing specific roots to be pulled out by the energy boost of forgiveness before the dance invitation can be accepted!

Recognize that to have a fully open, loving and compassionate heart centre, is to have a fully open, loving and compassionate third, second and first chakra energy centre also. And since release is not like the waving of a magic wand, the reality is that 'release' is staggered within each of our energy centres. And yet, what affects one, affects another also. Similarly, our capacity to love ourselves and to feel genuine compassion for ourselves and others is a staggered process also.

The good news is: with each release, we make progress on the efficiency of our energy flow of any individual energy centre! As you reach each stage of healing, you will be rewarded with a sensation of lightness that feels brand new to you and you will know ... *some old root has been successfully removed from your garden!* In its stead, you will have room to plant something beautiful as your visual reminder of being able to forgive. Take time to acknowledge yourself in your own healing process!

The sensation of release is felt via incremental discoveries through living in the presence of now.

Remember, the more roots you remove, the easier it will become for branches in your Water Element to be removed also ... and as your inner steam flows more consistently, the flame of your Fire Element's pilot light will be more consistent ... and with a consistent and controlled pilot light burning, the breath of your Air Element will be experienced more freely, and more deeply, opening you to a sensation of lightness (light) within yourself ... more loving and compassionate.

The miracle of Self-Care Reiki energy healing is that with each release we experience, another part of our energy system is affected. And although it is often unknown what is happening on our inner energy level, **as long as we continue with our healing process — of the need to forgive and *the willingness to forgive* — another root is eased out as well,** or another branch removed from our inner waterway, etc.

The relationship between compassion and forgiveness is logical and simple. Bottom line, if you cannot emotionally place yourself in your perpetrator's shoes, and feel the weariness or the stress of those shoes, then you are not yet ready to find it in your heart to feel compassion for the wearer of those shoes. *This is the energy-healing journey of which you are a part ...*

In a sense, the words of our poem are telling us this ...

I am in you and you are in me!
Together we engage in this journey.
Together, we teach each other,
Reflect each other's
Imperfections and perfections
As we strive for harmony
As we try to remember that
We are in all that is.

'Reflecting each other's imperfections' may be the source and clue of your inability to feel the stress of those shoes. *Time is still needed for you to acknowledge your own imperfections!* When you cannot yet grasp that you and the one with whom you are upset share some traits in common, you cannot feel compassion. Until you can feel compassion, you cannot find it in your heart to forgive (yourself or another). *And so it goes ...*

Air Element and heart chakra functional energies show up in everything you do and are in your Self-Care Reiki journey of healing and repair. They

- fan the flame of your inner pilot light, the Fire Element, bringing inner light to

- highlight obstacles that restrict the flow of your Water Element; they

- offer you the choice of removing those obstacles from both Earth and Water Elements and prevent more from developing; they

- aerate the inner soil of your Earth Element by strengthening your foundational energies — the way you feel about yourself — allowing you to find needed courage and resolve!

- In turn, *each of these elemental and chakra energies allow self-care healing of freely-flowing loving, compassionate and peaceful energies of Reiki to circulate throughout your being.*

Don't be discouraged if all of this doesn't happen immediately for you as you diligently place your gentle hands upon your body each day in Reiki Meditation and use the Precepts as affirmations and mantras.

The heart centre is often pictured as a beautiful, open lotus blossom. Remember, this lotus blossom was once a bud! It takes time for buds to open slowly as nature would have them open ... responding to the elements that surround them ... opening to the warmth ... slowing again with the cool temperatures. *Your Self-Care Reiki gentle touch stimulates your elemental warmth, each time you place your hands upon your budding inner self.*

Finally, I want to take a moment to look at what happens to us when we lack compassion for ourselves. One thing I consistently hear from students is that **it is very easy to be compassionate with others; it is more difficult to be compassionate with oneself.** *Why is this? Why is it easier to care for another than it is to care for oneself?*

Many of us were not raised to have compassion for ourselves. We need, therefore, to experience a new level of awareness (through the presence of now reality) such that the shift in self-compassion can occur in our own energy. And as often happens as we acquire a new awareness, the Universe will provide opportunities to test our new learning. If we are successful in applying our new teaching and awareness, we are rewarded instantly with the needed 'energy shift.' *This is part of the self-care journey of energy healing.* When we 'get it' the shift is automatic.

With each new shift of opening energy, it his rather like building a puzzle, where suddenly you can see where some of the pieces fit. As more pieces find their home place in the puzzle, they expose the pieces that have not yet fit into place. As you continue to remain aware of your objective of a finished puzzle, the Universe will offer you many opportunities to discover those energy pieces that need to find their perfect fit – their perfect home space – within your heart. (Opportunities to forgive another or yourself, for example, helps locate the missing pieces.)

Energetically, the ability to be compassionate with others and not with oneself, can become a source of burnout, especially for those working in 'front-line' professions. The constant giving of oneself to others, while not understanding the need to take care of one's 'self' also, is like travelling down a one-way street with no ability to turn around.

The routine practice of self-care in its many forms, teaches you to give back to yourself at the same time as giving of yourself to others. If these two forms of giving are not equal, they are out of balance ... which means **you** are out of balance!

The desire to give to others suggests an open and loving heart. Yet, as important as this is to serve others, it is critical to cultivate this same ability to serve yourself also! Otherwise, your imaginary house we referenced a short time ago, will be in constant need of repair, when the solution is so simple, really ... to remember to take time in your busy life to care for yourself also — or in house terms, to maintain the general upkeep of your inner home. **This, my reading friend, is why a Self-Care Reiki practice is so accommodating.** In your exhaustion at the end of the day, you can simply place your hands on your heart centre and receive an energy revitalization in keeping with your needs as you drift off into a welcomed sleep. You don't have to call a plumber, metaphorically speaking. *Each time you place your hands on your body, you are performing the energy-equivalent of self-repair!*

As we end our session today, in the presence of now, let's take another moment together to breathe more slowly and deeply — at least one hand against your heart centre — as you imagine your heart-felt energy flowing freely in your body, carried by your breath ... as you say the words out loud or inwardly: *I am showing compassion to myself and others ...*

You may wish to make your affirmation more specific in terms of *how* you are showing compassion to yourself ... make it real and something you can connect with to help you complete your puzzle sooner!

Continue to hold this position after you finish reading, placing your second hand over one of your other chakras that may be calling to you today ... allowing the messages of today's reading to sink in ...

Bottom Line Teaching

A Self-Care Reiki practice trains us to live in a 'presence of now' reality, finding love and compassion in our relationship with ourself as well as others, using forgiveness as a form of release ... recognizing that these are the qualities of our 'inner home' heart space of truth and peace.

Show compassion towards yourself and others by demonstrating loving kindness:

* towards yourself,
* towards your family members,
* towards your friends,
* towards strangers,
* towards your pets and animals in your care,
* towards all sentient creatures, and
* towards the environment in all of its forms ...

There is a kindly gentleness (and a gentle kindness) with all of these opportunities to show love and compassion. **As you heal, you will come to realize that you cannot allow yourself the luxury of even one unkind thought — about yourself or about others!** Think about this! How different life could be without any egocentric, negative thinking, commentary, reactions, etc; instead, only spiritual compassionate action and reaction. *This is kindness, genuine kindness, compassionate kindness.*

Build yourself and others up ... with kindness and compassion! Be a champion of kindness and compassion!

Hold these thoughts and your gentle hands-on touch position as you enjoy the healing energy of Reiki a little longer ...

In our next session, we will look at the Ether Element and begin to speak about gratitude. Until then, please look for new ways of being compassionate, kind, loving and gentle with yourself.

Namaste!

Show Compassion to Yourself and Others

YOGA with Louise Murray
Yoga Posture: The Cobra
The Element: Air
Chakra: Fourth / Heart Space
Self-Care Reiki Precept:
Show compassion to yourself and to others.

Just like the cobra rising up to defend itself, in this position of strength, allow yourself to mentally and emotionally rise up to greet compassion for yourself ... *in defence of yourself* ... and in this position of heart opening ... breathe the Air Element throughout your body with an awareness of your increasing strength as you hold this posture ...

Instructions:

- Lie on your stomach. Bend your elbows, and place them directly under your shoulders. Place your forearms on the floor, parallel to one another, hands are flat, palms down, fingers spread with index fingers pointing forward. If it's too intense for you, move your hands forward away from you.
- Shoulders are down away from your ears, and legs are hip-distance apart.
- Looking forward a few inches beyond the line of the fingertips, lift your chest forward. Feel your chest opening and expanding with each breath.
- If you wish to deepen the pose, slowly straighten your arms keeping your elbows slightly bent.

Just like the cobra rising up ... hold the pose for approximately two minutes, if you can.

In this position, acknowledge the parts of you that are crying out for love and self-compassion ...

*... **touch these areas in your mind with the gentleness of your opening heart space** as you use the words of the Reiki precept in the form of an affirmation, **I am showing compassion to myself** ...*

*... **allow the healing energy of Reiki to be carried by your heart beat flowing warmly to these spaces within you that have been neglected over time** ... as you hold this position for the next two minutes maximum ... eyes closed ... your full intention to bring energy healing awareness of self-compassion throughout your body and mind as you repeat your affirmation as mantra ... **I am showing compassion to myself.***

*Then, gently lower your body and turn over on your back, stretching your arms out wide on either side of your body, palms up in receiving mode, (knees bent, if more comfortable), surrendering your body and mind to completely open your heart space ... **feel the presence of now in this posture ... the presence of compassion for yourself** ...*

*... **rest and receive the effects of this compassionate Universal Life Force of the Air Element energy-healing awareness flowing freely throughout your body and mind** ... as you breathe slowly and comfortably ... straightening your legs again, if possible ...*

*... sense a balancing of compassionate energy flowing outwards from your heart to your life and to those who support you ... then received back again ... in a rhythmic and healing flow of energy back and forth ... **I am showing compassion to myself and to others** ...*

*... **increasing your awareness of your need for compassion as a way of life ... as a way of your life ... as a way of living an authentic life of inner truth and peace** ...*

* * * * * * * * * * * * * * * * * * * *

NOTE: For all postures in this book, Louise advises the following:

"It's always recommended to use a counter-pose in most cases. I recommend Knee Circles. *(Please refer to photo on page 45.)*

* **As you rest on your back, pull your knees into your chest.**
* **Place one hand on each knee and make circles with your knees together, first clockwise, then counter clockwise.**

Smaller circles massage your lower back close to the spine and larger circles massage outward toward the hips. Experiment to see what feels the best and enjoy your self-massage."

... then turn over on your side for a moment before slowly sitting up, eyes closed, a smile on your lips as you bring your hands together in front of your chest and give thanks for this awareness of renewed energy flow in your body.

Please be gentle with yourself. Namaste!

Energy Wellness Tip

In this earth
In this soil
In this pure field
Let's not plant
Any seed
Other than seeds
Of compassion
And love.

—RUMI

Self-Care Reiki Meditation

In the silence of spirit
I connect
In the silence of spirit
I am held
In the silence of spirit
I am home
In the silence of spirit
I behold
In the silence of spirit
I am truth
In the silence of spirit
I am peace
In the silence of spirit
I am love
In the silence of spirit
I am present
In the silence of spirit,
I am now.

We arrive at the living presence of now on the wings of the Ether Element ...

In this juncture of the Ether Element, where the natural and healing elements meet — where cold north winds blow, forming ice crystals called snow, where sky meets sea, where water meets land, where sun dances in breezes of the air, and rain droplets transform into rainbows — in these obvious evidences of elements inter-connecting in space, we too, connect easily, in the silent healing presence of Self-Care Reiki, without having to do anything other than be mindfully grateful for the healing space that both surrounds us and is real within us, in the living presence of now.

*These are the loving energies of the fourth chakra and its partner, the Air Element. They are also the energies of the third chakra of loving warmth and light and its partner, the Fire Element, and second chakra energy with its flowing inner energy pathways and its partner, the Water Element. And finally, we have discussed the energies of the first chakra, with its protective home-sheltering, foundational loving energy rooted within its key partner, the Earth Element ... all of these loving elemental energies are 'held' within the invisible space of the Ether Element ... reflecting to us how **we also are held within this same loving, invisible and etheric space of peace, in the truthful, healing presence of now ... the healing space of Self-Care Reiki.***

CHAPTER SIX

Gratitude as a Way of Being

PART ONE

In session six, the Ether Element is introduced as the natural space that holds all the other elements. As such, this natural space holds the energy of Universal Life Force. This definition can be further applied to the existential concept of oneself 'being held' (by the Universe) as we make our way through life. Caught within the ethers and 'holding us' may also be the presence of our ancestors, whose energy reaches out to commune with us from time to time as we move through life, perhaps even offering us strength that once was theirs.* Ancestral guidance may be interpreted as intuition, perhaps, or simply as a new idea that has popped into our head. 'Being held' by an unseen strength is a concept that takes us beyond physical communication — the physiological understanding of Fifth Chakra energy — to the etheric space of trust in 'something more,' an unseen force communing, guiding and affecting us holistically, as a way of being.

For anyone who is feeling alone, or who may be grieving something or someone no longer with you, the notion that you are always being held by the etheric space that surrounds you can be quite comforting. As we open to a conscious awareness of this healing space, healing transformation is possible. **Using Reiki's literal translation of Universal Life Force (energy) connecting with Vital Life Force (energy), it is where these two energies meet, that healing is possible.** From this understanding, the final affirmation or precept of the Usui System of Natural Healing is most meaningful: *Show gratitude to every living thing.* The Chapter ends with a combination of Self-Care Reiki touch and a simple Yoga posture that stimulates the Ether Element and our sense of 'being held by something more.'

* *Thank you, for this teaching, Great Grandmother Margaret*

Come rise to the rhythm of my soul
Touch me in sacred places
Come listen to my breath and
the pounding of my heart ...
Carry me on wisps of clouds ...
Take me to places beyond the horizon
Where time stands still and oceans swell ...
Listen to the rhythms of my soul. [28]

— Eithne L Barker

Welcome back, and as you attend to your reading retreat preparations today, prepare also to move into the space of the Ether
Element, as described in the beautiful verse above ... and the
final precept, *Show gratitude to every living thing.* A sound-healing suggestion today is called Throat Chakra Tibetan Singing
Bowls with Ocean Sounds.[29] A beautiful alternative to this is
any of Suzanne Teng's music; my suggestion being 'Above the
Clouds.'[30]

First, though, as you light your candle, this is an opportunity
to *feel the presence of now of the Ether Element in the silent peace
and beauty it emits* ... then, place your hands in Gassho, close
your eyes in reverence of this sacred healing space you are creating in these actions ... take a slower breath ... and **welcome
a moment of silent reflection with an intention to receive a
deeper understanding today of what your Self-Care Reiki
journey is all about ...**

Ether, as the element of space, is rather like a virtual hug. We
know how to hug others, yet it's not something we might do for
ourselves. So, our gentle self-care touch position today is one
of holding ourselves in a hug, after which we'll make the connection between the idea of 'being held' and gratitude.

> The easiest way to give yourself a hug, is to place
> your left hand on your right shoulder, and your right
> hand on your left shoulder. You cannot hold a book
> or a tablet as you do this, obviously, so just take a few
> minutes — before continuing to read — to experience
> this position for a few uninterrupted minutes, as you
> **allow yourself to fully relax into the comfort of**

your own arms in this sacred retreat space ... then, close your eyes and enjoy the comfort of this healing, Self-Care Reiki hug. Allow your head to rest into the comfort of one of your hands on your shoulder, rather like a bird tucking her head into her wing, and allow your body to sway back and forth gently, or from side to side as you relax ... fully aware of how this is feeling in this present moment. Remain in your self-care hug for as long as is comfortable ...

Reflection

How has this felt for you to embrace yourself in this way? Were you able to feel a sense of self-caring compassion?

The Ether Element is the space that holds and supports us at all times in our lives and especially in our most challenging times. It supports us as we grieve; it allows us to feel the prayers and love from those who are in sympathy with us. And, it allows us to remain in communion with one who is deceased until our humanness has an opportunity to adjust to the loss and learn to live with him or her, in spirit.

The Ether Element is also the space where beauty lives and is experienced. This ethereal healing space can be found anywhere that your awareness alerts you to the beauty of her space, where you can connect and feel the sensation of her beauty through any of your senses, and where you can live for a few precious moments in the presence of now. **It isn't the need for physical hands to touch you; instead you are being touched and held by nature's comforting energy** as understood in the lines from our opening poem written by an advanced Reiki student and dear friend, who was responding to such a connection.

Being held!

Have you ever experienced a situation that was shaping up to be frightening for you and almost magically, something happened to alter this for you without any previous planning or knowledge? I have a very special memory of this that I'd like to share with you.

It was an extremely cold Canadian winter's day. I was returning home from the library only a few blocks from my home. The weather had changed while I was enjoying my time in the library and when I left to walk home, I was greeted by a blast of severe, cold, north wind. I quickly realized I was insufficiently dressed to face this acute change in weather. Despite the reality that I could almost see my home, I wondered how I would ever make it there; the freezing cold wind seemed to be taking my breath. In the midst of my quickly building fear, my father drove by, saw me and stopped! In that moment ... as though time stood still ... it was like I was watching a version of myself climb into his warm car, greeted by his loving smile. Looking back at this surreal moment of my early life, I am still in awe at how my father 'just happened' to be driving by at exactly the moment in which I experienced such fear; it felt like a miracle! *This is but one example of 'being held.'* I expect you have some as well.

When unplanned happenings such as this occur, it is as though we are always being held by the loving arms of the Universe and when we need help, we don't even need to ask! ... *let this thought sink in ...*

From our last reading retreat's discussion of compassion for oneself and others, **the expression, 'being held,' conjures up beautiful and intangible images of caring.** It fully engages the heart centre of the body in a gesture of receiving or giving; this is the area where you've been hugging your own body — both giving to yourself and receiving — supported by the core energies of your lower chakras functioning harmoniously with your heart centre ....

Let's just have you resume this position again for a another few moments, and this time, **really notice how this feels to you ... actually hugging yourself ... holding yourself in caring and compassion ...** try to acknowledge this fully ... and breathe this awareness throughout your body ... then, open your awareness further to a sense of gratitude for the body and mind that you occupy ... your 'temple' that supports and holds you *all the time ... does it feel as though you are being held?*

Continue to hold one hand on your heart centre as you read, allowing your heart-centred energy to continue to flow ...

This supportive concept of 'being held,' resembles Self-Care Reiki energy completely. Using Reiki's literal translation of Universal Life Force connecting with Vital Life Force, the space where these energies meet is both within us and outside of us. **As we place our hands gently upon our body with conscious awareness, we are facilitating this 'remembered' and natural connection of energies, creating a healing space where healing transformation is possible ...** *and beyond our control.* **This is fundamentally Usui's System of Natural Healing.**

We are all agents of this healing energy that holds us and each other and like my story of being rescued from the freezing cold, one day, you may be the one who needs to be rescued. A stranger stops on a busy highway to help you when you have a flat tire, or someone encourages you to trust that all will be well, when you're concerned about something. Or, there may be times when you are the one who rescues others. The thought of a friend comes into your mind and you feel the need to call them, only to find that they are having a rough day. These are every-day examples of 'being held' by this Universal energy that touches us inside, elevating our spirits within and filling us with gratitude for receiving help and 'being held,' or for the ability to offer help ... to 'hold' another in our compassionate thoughts and actions.

As you are able to acknowledge this idea of being held, you are immersed in ethereal energy. This is essentially core energy — suggestive of energy that is made up of each of the four elements — earth, water, fire and air held in balance — from which gratitude flows easily, as a direct result of being held. **Any time that compassion and kindness are shown to or from another, the energy of the Ether Element — *of being held* — is at work.**

Gratitude intensifies these feelings of kindness and compassion. "It touches us in sacred places,"[31] to quote from our introductory poem. In fact, gratitude intensifies our experience within the Ether Element, in general. For example, **it is one thing to place ourselves in a beautiful space in nature,** where all the elements meet and healing is possible. We know from numerous online examples of "forest medicine research," that being in nature is a stress reliever, whether or not we are aware of the beauty of nature. **It is quite another experience to be consciously aware of nature's beauty;** in addition to receiving the natural healing powers of trees, **our *awareness* of forest beauty stimulates our sense of gratitude** for the experience of being there. Energetically, **gratitude intensifies our experience.**

We leave the area of nature not only with less measurable stress in our body / mind,[32] we leave with a more buoyant spirit as well for *we have engaged in the emotional experience of the beauty* as well. **This is a function of gratitude joining with the Ether Element to nourish all parts of us, 'to hold' all parts of us.**

For anyone who is feeling alone, or who may be grieving something or someone no longer with you, the notion that you are always being held by the etheric space that surrounds you — of 'something more' — can be quite comforting. **Being open to receive this unseen comfort of something more, opens you further to the mysteries that accompany it ... the healing presence of something much bigger than yourself ... where inner healing is possible ... where trust in something outside** of yourself feels more than simply comforting ... it feels like coming home to yourself — *your inner home* — where you are loved, understood and accepted ... where you are never alone in your sorrows or your celebrations ... where love is unyielding and gratitude is an unspoken reality, expressed throughout *all that is.*

How can we find this sacred healing space? Here are some suggestions.

In times of distress, nature can become a transformative healing space for you. *Go there in your times of feeling isolation or sadness.* For example, *trust an inner prompting to follow a cleared pathway that is safe, inviting you to come into its healing space of trees, or pasture, or meadow, etc., and be held by the living presence of now.*

On a clear night, look up into the vastness of the night sky and allow yourself to be held by its sense of ever-present eternity. *Look up both night and day, to receive and enjoy the timeless beauty of the Universe that forever holds you ... in the living presence of now.*

A familiar sound such as a robin singing at dawn, carried through the air within the elemental space of ether, may remind you of a time when you felt protected and secure. *Simply open your conscious awareness to listen ... then feel the delightful notes reaching out to you ... like the gentle presence of invisible arms wrapping around you in a sacred healing space ... bringing stillness and peace to your soul.* **Active listening is an example of *living the presence of now.***

Musical sounds are an example of this also, especially when the music is the kind that you enjoy ... creating a healing space that lifts you up, *holds you,* and inspires.

'Making music' by singing or playing an instrument, can create such an opening for you. *As you listen, try to experience this sense of being held by the beautiful sounds ... instinctively connecting you with 'something more' ... instilling ethereal comforts through all parts of you ... in the living presence of now.*

'Coming in out of the cold' to a warm hearth offers a means of being enveloped / held by the ethereal warmth that a safely burning fire can provide ... *sit within its warmth and ethereal possibilities of being held ... in the living presence of now.*

Walking the beach or mountain trail, may offer the kind of comfort you need to feel held by the elements ... *share your truth within these majestic spaces that are able to absorb your torments and tears without judgement or condemnation ... supporting you completely as you give way to release of long-held grief, guilt or any form of emotional trauma you have endured and held ...* to be released into the invisible ethers to dissolve for all of time *in the living presence of now.*

Closing your eyes and remembering faces of loved ones no longer present, whose countenance warms and comforts you. *See their faces in your mind, allow their faces to hold you in this moment now, as you remember them ... holding you by the comforting memories they offer you ... memories that are associated with being held physically, perhaps, or emotionally, through sounds of recalling their voice, or of food they enjoyed or prepared for you ... and of much, much more ... in the living presence of now.*

What each of these suggestions 'holds' in common, is the sense of feeling connected *by* and *in* the living presence of now! We may search for something outside of us to feel this way, yet **true connection is a sense that is *within us.* It is alive, like a *presence* within us and it is *now!***

These suggestions merely remind us that this is so ... for we can find ourselves in a crowd of people we know and care for, and not feel 'connected.' **Please realize that in times of feeling emotionally disconnected from your sacred inner space of home, you are *always* being held by the energy of something more than the way you currently feel ... *like an eternal presence of now accompanying you as you find your way back home ...***

Returning to our poem:

You are in the mists of time!
I am in the mists of time!
We are in the mists of time!

Together ... each one of us <u>can</u> answer the call to return to
the Source,
The call that is felt and heard in our desperate sense of
disconnection ...
Of separation ...
Of loss ...
Of grief ...
Of depression ...
Of despair ...
In our desperate need to return ...
To the Source of all that is;
For it is here that we find
The peace we search for,
The joy waiting to be expressed,
The love available to all.

In our more sublime moments, it is easy to believe that we are being held by the energies of 'something more' that we keep alluding to ... something more that is too large to even comprehend ... yet small enough to be found in a grain of sand or a blade of grass ... all to be enjoyed by each one of us as we travel the space of the earth that is very much a part of the Universe ... and through our enjoyment, **our emotions open us *to live the presence of now, to feel* this full connection or re-connection with something more,** in our heart space ... *in astonishing gratitude.*

Gratitude is our final Self-Care Reiki Precept and affirmative way of being. It goes like this: *Show gratitude to every living thing.* We make it more powerful by using the words, 'I am,' as a prefix to create an affirmation: *I am showing gratitude to every living thing.*

Gratitude, as a way of being, stills the mind. It opens the mind to see both who and what is all around us, and has been there all along yet often goes unnoticed. We may neglect those who are closest to us, taking them for granted in our life and assuming they will always be there. Gratitude for their presence is a life-changing thought of appreciation for who these people are and what they mean to us.

Gratitude for your life's mission and ministry — whatever this is currently, has been in the past, or may be in the future — awakens you to aspects of your daily work and meaning for getting up each morning.

And gratitude for all who support you in your life — such as your friends and family, your work colleagues, neighbours, community, special interests, etc., and for your abilities that allow you to function to the best of any limitations you may have, to maintain your health and wellbeing, for the body and mind you occupy. I could go on ...

Bottom Line Teaching

A Self-Care Reiki practice invites you to weave gratitude into everything you do and are, and begin to experience life in a new way. You will soon discover new reasons to smile. You may find yourself genuinely sharing your inner smile with a stranger or with the cashier in the grocery store who looks like he or she is not having a good day, then saying something complementary that may help him or her engage with you in a smile also. This is an example of the cashier 'being held' in this moment by the Universe ... by something more, *through you!!*

Reflection

Please take time today to reflect upon your own life, where you may have experienced this sense of being held. For example, perhaps your plans suddenly changed and you were guided to go somewhere else or to do something different than what was planned, yet turned out to be exactly what you needed ... or what someone else needed. *In retrospect, could you say that you were being held or that you were holding some-one?* Perhaps you could journal the specifics of any experience of this phenomenon.

As you take this opportunity to reflect and bring these moments to light, please also engage in a sense of gratitude for what was happening to you ... *for how you were being held, or able to hold another.* **In awakening to such moments with gratitude, you will begin to awaken to the frequency with which these happenings actually occur synchronistically in your life,** as the Universe either holds you, or enlists you to hold others, in the simplest of ways.

As you awaken to these moments in gratitude, you begin to polish your inner lens to clearly see, live and acknowledge these moments 'in the moment' as they are happening, and consequently to give thanks in real time, *in the presence of now.*

To whom are you giving thanks? ... to the broadest understanding of 'the Universe' ... realizing that all that has life makes up 'the Universe,' some of which can neither be seen nor understood.

The subject of gratitude is far too vast to cover in the space of one session, so we will continue this discussion in our next chapter. In the meantime ...

> Allow yourself a little longer in this healing space of holding yourself ... either emotionally or physically re-engaging in your Self-Care Reiki hug .... consciously allow the energy of gratitude to hold you also, feeling grateful, as you hug yourself comfortably and with compassion for yourself ... then mindfully breathe gratitude slowly and deeply ... imagine the energy of gratitude flowing easily throughout your body and mind ... relaxing you further into this healing Self-Care Reiki position of comfort, love, compassion and gratitude ... each energy of which is holding you right this minute ... as we end our session today in the comfort of gentleness, stillness and peace.

Please be gentle with yourself. Namaste!

Gratitude as a Way of Being, Part One

YOGA with Louise Murray

Yoga Posture: Easy Seated Pose (sitting cross legged)

The Element: Ether

Chakra: Fifth / Throat

Self-Care Reiki Precept:
Show gratitude to every living thing.

Instructions:

In this familiar posture, sitting cross legged (Easy Seated Pose), you have a choice of sitting on the ground, on your yoga mat on the floor (you can use a firm cushion or folded blanket under your buttocks), on the bed or in a chair.

When you are comfortably seated, as above, you can add Universal Energy of the Ether Element by moving your right hand to your left calf, and your left hand to your right calf as a Self-Care Reiki gentle touch position. (In addition to the beautiful energy already present within this posture, this cross-over effect further stimulates the flow of ether energy.)

Close your eyes, and begin to breathe more slowly and deeply a few times to help you settle in and relax, then relax your breath and breathe normally, dropping your shoulders, loosening your lower jaw, relaxing your upper body, arms, hands and fingers ... and your lower body, feet and toes ... **feeling grateful for every living thing,** *understanding the meaning of these words in your life ...*

Notice how your body reacts to this posture ... if you feel any tight-ness anywhere, make a slight adjustment if necessary, and breathe directly into the space that feels tight ... otherwise ...

Simply relax and enjoy the flow of ether energy beginning to circulate in your body and mind ... remain in this position for as long as feels comfortable, knowing you can return to it anytime your lower body needs a hug also (as you are doing now), to stimulate this beautiful flow of Self-Care Reiki energy within a classic Yoga posture, feeling a sense of gratitude for this moment, *living this presence of now. ...*

Rest and enjoy.

● ● ● ● ● ● ● ● ● ● ● ● ● ● ● ● ● ● ●

NOTE: For all postures in this book, Louise advises the following:

"It's always recommended to use a counter-pose in most cases. I recommend Knee Circles. *(Please refer to photo on page 45.)*

● **As you rest on your back, pull your knees into your chest. Place one hand on each knee and make circles with your knees together, first clockwise, then counter clockwise.**

● **Smaller circles massage your lower back close to the spine, and larger circles massage outward toward the hips. Experiment to see what feels the best and enjoy your self-massage."**

Please be gentle with yourself. Namaste!

Ether Energy Wellness Exercise of Gratitude

Do you have any idea how incredibly beautiful you are?

This is a question that arises when you spot a beautiful creature such as the white egret that appears in the photo at left. In fact, as you study this magnificent bird, rather than simply see 'her' in passing, you will notice how she hunts for her meal in shallow waters with both stealth and grace. And if you continue to watch, you will notice how her grace remains present as she takes flight, her huge wingspread manoeuvring her lift-off with unparalleled grace and gentleness; her quiet and immense strength concealed within her beauty, equipping her ability to fly the long distances required to migrate both spring and fall. *Does the egret know how beautiful she is?* She is beautiful ... *she just is ... without even trying!*

So, with this as background, try going through the day looking for beauty in everything and in every one — *including yourself!* As you look in the mirror, look beyond the image you see. Look for your strengths and your inner beauty. It is all there for the realization! Humbly, see how incredibly beautiful you are, *without even trying!* **You just are!!**

As you do this exercise, **feel a beautiful sense of gratitude for your inner beauty ... your many gifts and talents you were born with that are yours and yours alone ... gifts that allow you to express yourself in ways that only you can.** *This is one way of showing gratitude to every living thing as part of your Self-Care Reiki practice.*

This simple exercise will peak your powers of observation ... to notice more acutely the beauty that exists throughout nature as well as the beauty that exists in all the people in your life ... and in noticing, to feel grateful!

It may also call upon your ability to feel compassion, on your quest to see, hear, sense, taste, or feel beauty. Beauty, as you will come to realize, is experienced through a sense of living the connection, *in the presence of now!*

Ether is soul food, a healing space of beauty
in all of beauty's meanings.

It is the space of silence in cathedrals,
stone circles, gardens and forests,

reaching out and touching us in our heart.

It is our visual, auditory, touch, olfactory,
and verbal expressions of meaning.

It is healing energy that meets us where we
are and accepts us ... just as we are.

It is healing energy that heals us where we are ...

Ether is the element that always brings comfort; it sings
our personal lullaby and restores us as we sleep.

When we deny ether's influence in our life, we for-
get how to pause and breathe in our reality ...

We deny how beautiful we are ...

We forget to acknowledge our physical body
and mind as having a shelf life

that comes closer to expiration with each passing day ...

CHAPTER SEVEN

Gratitude as a Way of Being

PART TWO

A Self-Care Reiki practice trains us to live in a 'presence of now' reality, *feeling* grateful for all that is ... capturing moments that build upon the positive, opening us to greater depths of awareness of all that is *in the eternal presence of now.*

Following on the wisps of the existential quality of the Ether Element in our previous reading, **Reiki and the Ether Element are inextricably linked in the beautiful practice of expressing of gratitude. Gratitude, as a feeling and energy *in the presence of now,* is transformative. Genuine gratitude can turn a difficult situation into something quite positive.** When you engage in a Self-Care Reiki practice, you become more comfortable in your own skin and gratefully *present* to the simple things in life and to others who share their life with you in any number of ways, from cutting your hair to packing your groceries ... showing gratitude to those you love as well as those you do not even know can transform energy within you and in those receiving your gratitude ... sometimes turning the day around in a very positive way.

As gratitude becomes a way of life,
you begin to see the good in everyone and in everything.
You embody a living affirmation of the final Reiki precept:
'Show gratitude to every living thing.'

Welcome back to your retreat space and our continuing discussion of the Ether Element and gratitude as key aspects of Self-Care Reiki energy flow. **Please light your candle in gratitude for what what you are feeling in this presence of now, that is calling for your attention.** Take these feelings into your Gassho practice today, as you pause for a moment of centering, feeling, acknowledging and giving thanks ...

And now, make sure you are comfortably settled in your physical retreat space, perhaps omitting meditation music today to instead engage with the ethereal space of silence. If you prefer some ethereal music, however, I recommend a short centering piece of music, called Lotus,[33] by Suzanne Teng. *(This track can be used repetitively in a playlist, set to the amount of time you wish to spend on meditation. For example, if your goal is ten minutes, you could repeat the playlist two times.)*

Today's mediation goal is to physically feel the Ether Element flow within your body.

To do this, place the palms of your hands together (right hand on top) with fingers in opposite directions ... then gently hold the **underside** of your left wrist with your right thumb tip and first finger tip, resting just inside the bony prominences on the both sides of your wrist. Then relax both hands on the midline of your abdomen ... relax your arms and shoulders as you do this ... close your eyes and breathe more slowly ... continuing to keep your hands as you have them now. Hold this position for a minimum of five minutes.

Alternatively ... you could try placing your right palm over the back of your left hand and gently hold the bony prominence on both sides of your wrist with right thumb tip and first finger tip. Then, as above, relax both hands against the midline of your body ... and relax your arms and shoulders as you begin to breathe more slowly and deeply. Hold for a minimum of five minutes.

Reflection

Were you able to sense something special during your time just now in meditation?

Please take a moment to breathe gratitude throughout your body and mind for whatever this was ... in fact, you might like to close your eyes again and 'be present' in this healing space of gratitude as you recall your experience.

The final precept, *Show gratitude to every living thing* includes **you**, and your life: *past, present and future.*

We don't always feel grateful for ourselves ... for all *we* are ... and for our simple blessings ... So let's pause for another moment with this in mind ... *be present to yourself ... let yourself actually feel a sense of gratitude for your entire being, in this presence of now,* before continuing.

Gratitude, perhaps more than any other single entity, teaches us to come into the *space of the presence of now* ... to live:

- the *healing space* of the presence of now ...
- the *etheric, healing space* of the presence of now ...
- the *conscious healing space* of the presence of now, where healing energies meet and peace resides ...
- **this is the *healing space* of Self-Care Reiki.**

Gratitude guides our focus to feel and experience one moment at a time ... the presence of now ... allowing us to be fully present and aware, with no competing 'noise' in our mind ... *where words are not necessary to convey how we feel ...* **words cannot adequately describe how the healing space of the present moment of now feels** ... or how the healing space of a special memory moment in our past felt at the time ... *or how that same memory feels now as we bring it forward into the present ... where gratitude still overflows in the presence of now ...*

***Our memory is preserved in mental pictures, sounds, and most of all, in feelings.* And although these feelings were enjoyed in the past, they are timeless and can still be enjoyed in the present.** *This has huge implications as we grieve the loss of someone who has been very special to us. We can still see their face in our mind, and hear their voice as well as highlights that were important to us in our relationship with the one who is now gone. And while the reliving of these moments may create temporary renewed sadness, they also preserve our remembered relationship in a 'space' within us that can be taken out and appreciated or shared as appropriate. As we healthily process our grief, this space can become a 'healing space' of gratitude for us to revisit on days we need the specific energy recall of this person to lift us up and remind us that everything is going to be okay.*

When we live in gratitude, our ability to remember these moments allows us to feel comforted by our memories and grateful to have actually lived these experiences, as opposed to living in maudlin feelings about the past.

When we live without gratitude, our memories can lead us into a state where we feel victimized by our sense of loss. "We grieve because we loved," to quote a cliche. And although grief is about connecting with the feelings of loss and sadness, grief calls us to not remain in this space forever; rather, to use our time in grieving to heal our loss and become grateful for the many blessings of what has been, so we can move forward in our life ... while acknowledging that time for emotional healing is part of the process of healing our grief.

Our Self-Care Reiki practice helps us find this state of present-moment peace and gratitude as we grieve, by tapping into the etheric flow of Reiki energy.

Our Self-Care Reiki practice naturally attunes us to see and hear and feel and live our lives with more openness and gratitude ... to come into the present and see what is before us, *in the presence of now,* as the following story will attest:

A Reiki student reported on her second class with me, how she noticed wild flowers growing by the roadside on her drive home following her first Reiki attunement, the previous week. Despite the fact that the wildflowers had always been there, my student had never consciously seen them before, although she drove beside them every day. They were oblivious to her perceptive reality prior to her attunement to Reiki. *In her moment of actually seeing and appreciating them, this woman was emotionally affected by their visual beauty,* such that she couldn't wait to tell me at her next session. **Nature was physically present to her each time she travelled this road, however, her mind was so pre-occupied with other thoughts of work and family demands, she could neither *feel* nor *see* nature reaching out to her.**

It was her Reiki attunement that brought her into the presence of now of her reality ... *her truth* about how she was living her life ... **playing itself out in the simplest of lessons that nature could offer to teach her.** The wildflowers by the roadside, in their quiet beauty and simplicity, spoke volumes to her mind and emotions that may never have been achieved in her therapist's office as she talked about her life.

On that life-changing day for her, she was able to receive — *to be held* — *by the etheric energy of nature,* in a transformative moment of conscious awareness and subsequent transformative healing ... *in the space where healing energies meet.*

Can you imagine her delight and joy? ... followed by her full acknowledgement that she had never seen this obvious beauty in nature before ... in this one moment of time in her life, **she was instantly connected to her inner truth ... to her desperate need to slow down and discover other ways she was missing out, by living an unbalanced and out-of-control lifestyle.** Feelings of gratitude for this realization were not only apparent in her telling of her story that day, **gratitude for what she was no longer prepared to miss in her life was a mounting reality that would forever change her life.**

Gratitude has the power to open ... to receive ... to transform ... to heal ...

Gratitude is exponential in its ability to open us to more and more in our life for which to be grateful ... *and in these moments to actually give thanks!* I find myself saying, "Thank you," out loud in my car each time I enter a busy freeway with enough space between vehicles that my access is easy. I also say, "Thank you," out loud when I find a parking space in an area that seems filled with cars. At these times, **I feel as though I am 'being held' by an invisible force, or sense of energy, guiding me in even the simplest of things I might do in any given day.**

I highlight this because **Self-Care Reiki can be / is a part of everything you do in any given day.** You don't have to be attuned to Reiki for these things to happen; however, an attunement helps. When I meet with groups of students I have taught and ask the question: "So how's your Reiki practice coming along?", it is rare that people speak to these things; rather, they refer to their hands-on practice.

Reiki is so much more than a hands-on practice! I hope by now, you are grasping this awareness, and yet, **the hands-on practice brings form to one's self-care** and reminds us that our body and mind have the capacity to heal and grow. The energy we bring every day to our body, mind, spirit and soul through a hands-on practice is always going to those places within us that need to be balanced, such that we *can* see those wildflowers growing by the side of the road.

Another form of Self-Care Reiki gratitude, as reflected at the end of this chapter, is to begin each day with gratitude such as: *Thank you for this new day and for all of the blessings flowing into it!*

This can be done as soon as you open your eyes in the morning, or as you sit on the edge of your bed before standing up, or after you have emerged from your bed and go to a window to look out into the day to check the weather. *Thank you for this new day and for all of the blessings flowing into it!*

You may wish to test this exercise tomorrow morning, then every morning for at least one week, and see if it doesn't open your awareness to see goodness in your day.

By placing your awareness on gratitude from your first instance of wakefulness, you are opening yourself in that moment — *to the feeling of gratitude in the presence of now* — and for the potential abundance of your day ... *opening your Self-Care Reiki elemental flow of Universal energy — the healing space where all the elements are held ...*

Look for gratitude in the simplest of things in your day today, for what has already transpired so far ... for example, *connect with the feeling of gratitude* for the comfort of your chair, for the first taste of your morning brew, for the wave from your friend, for a call from a family member. These are examples of things we take for granted ... until we don't have them ...

As you crawl into bed tonight, *feel* gratitude for the comfort of your bed and for the good night's sleep you are about to have, welcoming a sense of futuristic gratitude into your nighttime.

At the end of our last session, we talked about how smiling and speaking to a cashier who looks like they're not having a good day, can have an impact on them. **This is about your being**

a beacon of 'light' for another. Your genuine smile can lift them up, even for a moment — long enough to make a change in how they feel ... to shift their energy ... and reinforce how you feel, also.

Greeting a stranger on the sidewalk as you have a morning walk or run, can yield similar results of sending light into one another's day. Such feelings can last for a considerable length of time leaving a smile on your face also and in your body and mind, often lasting for several minutes ... setting a tone for how you feel for much longer after that, perhaps influencing your entire day.

Unspoken greetings happen at coffee drive-throughs all the time, with people paying for coffee for the stranger behind them in line ... **such an intentional activity celebrates gratitude in a very tangible way.** It sets off a series of smiles and surprises and joy for all involved, and **inspires recipient(s) to spread this light further** by paying for the person in the vehicle behind them also, or for sharing their inner light with others in *their* vehicle, home or workplace throughout their upcoming day.

From an Ether Element perspective, these are simple examples of 'being held' by the Universe ... feeling goodwill being generated *within you* by complete strangers and *through you* as you continue to spread goodwill to complete strangers. **These are the subtleties of a Self-Care Reiki practice** ... unlikely to be referred to as "Reiki, per se," yet holding all the components of Reiki as we defined it at the very beginning:

* *Reiki is healing energy,*
* *Reiki is meditation,*
* *Reiki is peace,*
* *Reiki is love and compassion,*
* *Reiki is gratitude,*
* *Reiki is a way of being,*
* *Reiki is mindfulness training,*
* *Reiki is our relationship with ourselves, with one another and with the Universe,*

* *Reiki is an energy that is alive, that heals, that awakens when we open ourselves to it,*
* *Reiki is an energy that guides … guides us **through** our opening awareness **towards** those things we need, and **away from** those things that may be harmful,*
* *Reiki is life-changing,*
* *Reiki guides us to live in the presence of now.*

I suspect that Reiki's founder, Mikao Usui, intended us to use gratitude as a way of being in order to feel and experience its powerful energy to transform us and others. **As we connect with this beautiful etheric energy, we are held by its ability to show us the light within our own darkness** … a constant inner light shining into our dark corners and **resurrecting us to a new way of being … helping us grow into the fullness of who we truly are, teaching us to look beyond what has been, to what can be …** *so we can feel joy in what is!*

When you **practice gratitude as a way of being in the presence of now** — showing gratitude to others and to all living things — this kindly lifestyle of gratitude will create a return on your moment-to-moment investment of time, as you begin to experience its energy returning to you in the way you feel as a result of your kindness offered to others.

Gratitude, as a lifestyle choice, creates a subtlety of Reiki energy working within you and through you to effect others … without any reference to Reiki as a healing energy whatsoever … like the invisible space of the Ether Element that holds all the elements together.

Reiki *is* the invisible energy that holds you … and by working *through you*, it helps others feel as though they are being held by something outside of their physical being also … especially meaningful on a day that is challenging or stressful. Such invisible outreach of Reiki energy to others as you go about your days will keep you filled as well.

Reiki energy is to be found in the stressless daily deeds of gratitude we will never know we have even performed … we all have times, I expect, where someone says something to us that is the perfect thing at the perfect time ... or smiles at us at a time we need it the most. The generator of these actions will never know how their behaviour has impacted another ... and the recipient will only know that they feel as though they are not alone in that magical moment ... an incentive to keep going, perhaps ... to light up their pilot light and spread warmth throughout their own being.

It is important for me to say that we do not need to be attuned to Reiki for any of these things to happen. Many of us go about our days smiling, sharing goodwill and speaking to strangers, enjoying the feelings that flow with no knowledge of Reiki.

Being attuned to Reiki has the potential to further align us with such activity, opening us to a deeper awareness of life, as we heard from the woman who saw wildflowers for the first time. Reiki attunements have the potential to awaken us at deeper levels of our being and increase our awareness in all of our senses ... allowing us to perhaps be more easily 'guided' to make a call to someone who has come into our mind ... only to find they were needing to hear from us today ...

As we end our retreat time together today, I'd like you to place one hand over your fourth chakra or heart centre which partners with the Air Element in the middle of your chest, and the other lightly over or just beneath your throat — your fifth chakra, which partners with the Ether Element ... This is a very calming position at any time and especially when you feel stressed. It is also a recommended healing space of comfort for one who is grieving a loss and needs to feel a sense of being held by the Universe. **(Notice the positioning of your body ... you are holding yourself)**

This is a healing space of peace that can hold you in times of gratitude also, as you remind yourself of the healing precept, as affirmation, *I am showing gratitude to every living thing* ... **remember that this includes you, yourself.**

Rest now ... take a slow and deep breath into this Self-Care Reiki position of gentle, healing touch ... close your eyes ... put your feet up and relax for as long as you need today ... relax and lower your shoulders so they are not feeling tense ... and **with each thought that comes into your mind, look for something to be grateful for within that thought ... then connect with the feeling of gratitude ... and breathe this feeling throughout your body and mind ... try to hold your genuine feeling of gratitude beyond this quiet time, and allow it to remain with you in your unfolding day ...**

Bottom Line Teaching

A Self-Care Reiki practice trains us to live in a 'presence of now' reality, *feeling* grateful for all that is ... capturing moments that build upon the positive, opening us to a greater depth of awareness of all that is *in the eternal presence of now.*

In our next session, we will talk about how Reiki can be used to help us sleep ... in the meantime, please remember to be grateful for all the simple things in your life to day ... and as you do this, please be gentle with yourself. Namaste!

Energy Wellness Tip

A Morning Ritual of Gratitude

Please face the eastern sky as you begin this standing meditation moment, while mentally connecting with the **Earth Element** beneath your feet ... then stretch your arms out wide as you say the following words:

Thank you for this new day, and for all the blessings flowing into it today.

(This, believe, it or not, is another way of stimulating etheric Reiki energy flow by opening this place of gratitude within yourself ...)

Then raise your arms up high, bringing your palms together over your head, pause for a moment as you breathe gratitude ... then lower your arms, palms still touching, resting them in front of your heart chakra in Gassho position. Smile! Pause here for another moment as you consciously breathe your smile ...

*Feel your smile awakening your **Water Element** to the emotion that is behind your smile ... stimulating the inner pilot light of your **Fire Element** to feel the warmth that flows from your genuine smile ... and connecting to your Air Element through your breath, feeling the love that is inherent in your smile — both love for your 'self' and love for humanity — contained within the **Ether Element of gratitude** for all that has life.*

Take this healing energy into your day ... every day ... release your hands only when ready ...

CHAPTER EIGHT

A Self-Care Reiki Lifestyle and Sleep

A Self-Care Reiki practice trains us to live in a 'presence of now' reality, even at bedtime, such that we can use our hands and our breath to relax our body /mind to settle into a peaceful healing space of much deserved sleep.

Sleep is as necessary for us as is nutritious food and regular exercise. As we sleep, our body is busily working on our behalf, restoring us as we sleep. It is a conscious down-time, where we can fully relax and allow all the healing possible within us, completely outside of our awareness. Because many people experience sleep issues, we will practice five Self-Care Reiki gentle touch positions to help you settle more easily for sleep, or return to sleep if you awaken in the night. As well, we'll look at some of the potential reasons that sleep may be illusive at times.

Sleep is the best meditation

Dalai Lama

Welcome back to 'our' Self-Care Reiki healing space *I* am enjoying with *you*, each time you return to this book!

And as you light your candle today, followed by the Gassho position, let's take a slow and deep breath ... and open with a moment of gratitude for this day that is upon us now at this very moment ... and for all the blessings flowing into this day ... into the future, unfolding events of this day ...and for the ability to find blessings where there is challenge ... then feel a sense of inner strength as you focus on the blessings *of* the challenge ... remain with these thoughts for a few moments of silent centering ... allowing the energy of Reiki to envelop you ... to hold and comfort you ... and remain with you throughout the day ...

Suggested music for today's meditation is Whispering Notes.[34]

We will be trying out five Self-Care Reiki positions for sleep at the end of this chapter. For now though, you may like to try a simple yoga position of lying down in front of a wall, and elevating your legs to rest either straight up against the wall or in a V-shape (against the wall.) To do this, you need to sit down with your hips as close to the wall as possible, then lie down on the floor and elevate your legs. Alternatively, you can lie on the floor and rest your legs against the seat of a couch or chair, bending your knees and having your lower legs rest comfortably on the seat cushion. Either position is one that can be used prior to going to bed at night to begin a sense of calming and centering after a busy day. It is also quite relaxing, as you will soon discover. If you are unable to do either of these positions, perhaps you would enjoy sitting down with your feet raised on a footstool. Once in one of these positions, you can place your Self-Care Reiki hands against your body wherever they wish to go today, or you can spread your arms out wide in a heart opening gesture or raise your arms above your head if you are feeling the need to stretch out your body.

Our Self-Care Reiki retreat today is focused on sleep, and in the words of Dalai Lama, "Sleep is the best meditation!" Think of this for a moment. *How many times have you gone to bed at night feeling upset about something, only to feel differently about it in the morning?*

I would add an additional thought to Dalai Lama's quote ... sleep is also the best form of self-restoration. Much internal repair is carried out as we sleep. The more peacefully we sleep, the easier this natural healing and restorative repair can take place. So it is good that we spend one of our retreat chapters discussing sleep positions for Self-Care Reiki, especially since so many people have sleep issues. I will not be broaching upon general health or nutritional reasons as to why this might be so. This information is well documented elsewhere.

Before we begin, however, I draw your attention back to the words of the verse below:

We are in all that is.
I am in you and you are in me!
Together we engage this journey.
We are in our friends and in our enemies
We are in all that is.

As we reflect upon these words, it may seem less surprising that one reason we may have difficulties either going to sleep at night or getting back to sleep after awakening in the night is that our thoughts are on others. We naturally care about those who are close to us ... and in caring, they are foremost in our mind. The words of the poem speak to this: '*I am in you and you are in me!*' To use an expression from our last two sessions concerning the energy of the Ether Element, *'we hold one another'* in our caring thoughts.

Secondly, augmenting this first reason, sometimes these thoughts lead us to worry or carry feelings of concern. **Learning to let go of worry as we suggested in chapter two, is one of our most challenging self-care practices to help us sleep.** For, despite our attempts to not worry, we may continue to do so ... and when we worry, our sleep is affected. In this book, through our Self-Care Reiki practice, we are attempting to help you reduce and stop worry habits; we are also attempting to help you find ways to improve your sleeping patterns.

Being concerned about others can be defined as broadly as one's thoughts will allow. Disturbing stories appear in the news almost daily, reminding us of the plights of others. If we watch the nightly news before going to bed, we may lie awake thinking of what we have just seen televised, then struggle to get to sleep. Or, we may not think about what we have seen; rather, we notice how agitated we feel and wonder why.

Or, we may chronically or habitually worry irrationally about family issues that seem insurmountable in the middle of the night. These are the issues that prevent us from going back to sleep once they 'get going' in our heads.

And thirdly, I would like to speak to various forms of energy that are a part of daily life beyond the news and problems of life. We'll begin with **overload,** as a possible reason for not sleeping well and forgive me, please, for digressing as I go into some detail about this subject as it affects the workplace.

In our modern world, overload has become an insidious reality in our day to day living. We may take on more than we can manage comfortably in an effort to please, or get ahead, or because 'there is no one else who can do it,' or so we can keep our job! As workplaces began to cut costs to compete prior to the turn of this century, 'corporate downsizing' became a new phrase with a subsequent reality of added responsibility being shouldered within a reduced complement of staff. Such supposedly 'seamless changes' — created a new diagnosis: 'workplace stress.'

As a former occupational health manager of a large corporation, I recall my boss and myself sitting across the desk from the HR Director discussing this subject. He outrightly denied that workplace stress existed, and ended our meeting hastily, now understanding why we requested the meeting with him. Not two weeks later, this same gentleman died of a heart attack! Of course, since that time, companies could no longer hide this reality as stress claims began to mount. Claims which originally had been denied by insurance companies and workers' compensation, began to be accepted. By 2018, workplace stress was cited as a main cause of mental health issues, in a study reported by the Globe and Mail, in 2018. [35]

I mention this reality, because *it is **a** reality*, and because I am very emotionally present to the severity of the problem, having suffered it myself. In fact, my own journey with Reiki began during my high stress job and I give full credit to Reiki for helping me during my last years of employment. It allowed me to find the 'something more' principle of living I keep referring to throughout this book.

And while I am on my 'soap box' I will say one more thing. I believe for some people, their religious practice is where they turn for 'something more.' The reality is that people may not always behave the way we expect they 'should' behave in the real world outside their place of worship. Devout believers in their faith tradition may seem fully compliant while they are within the edifice of worship, fulfilling leading roles there, then turn against 'their neighbour' once outside again, and in the workplace. Such behaviour is beyond unacceptable; it is hypocritical.

What I can tell you about a Self-Care Reiki practice, having practiced it now since 1993, is that it offers 'something more' everywhere you find yourself. It doesn't require a building to practice or profess a belief. Nor does it require a particular dress code. It allows you to be yourself and affects everything you do. This includes how you survive the stress of your workplace, *highlighting inequities and intolerances for you* such that you can more easily make a decision to remain or to leave, trusting that there is another way to do your job or to offer your skills elsewhere.

I'll step down from my soap box now.

Our homes can take on overload as well, often reflecting to us a lifestyle to which we have become oblivious ... a lifestyle of so much going on, that little time is left over to care for ourselves adequately. One of the very positive outcomes of the Covid-19 Crisis has been the 'global step back and pause' phenomenon. The effect has been one of acknowledging the societal pace we have been living as a global society, and an opportunity to recalibrate our individual and collective intentions for moving forward.

If overload has been an issue for you, perhaps it is time to look at your schedule and ask yourself if there is something you are ready to change, improve or let go.

From a self-care perspective, as you do this, **consider whether each activity is an *energizing* activity or if, in fact, it is an energy drain.** In other words, *how does each activity make you feel? Does it give you energy and support you, or does it leave you feeling bereft of any reserve of energy?*

Sometimes one's well-intentioned involvement in community work, as an example, can become quite draining. Extra-curricular, volunteer activity needs to be a win-win situation; you do something of value for an organization or a group, and in return, you are fed *energetically* by the activity. **If the energy of the activity is no longer serving *you* also, perhaps this would be the time to consider decluttering your mental / emotional life by eliminating the activity!** Try something new, perhaps, or even take a pause ... 'down time' for relaxation.

What is important in this discussion, is that any of these actions might impact your ability to sleep better. **Often we don't realize we carry burdens that affect our sleep, until the burden has been removed** ... which leads me to my fourth reason I am presenting as a deterrent to sleep ... **the decluttering of your physical home space, especially your sleeping space.**

We are living in a time of consumerism, often buying or receiving gifts amounting to more than we really need ... while possibly not clearing out unused or outdated belongings to accommodate an influx of the new. Consequently, homes are often stuffed with small appliances, unusable technology, clothing, toys, sports equipment, to name only a few categories, any of which occupy space in the home. **When unusable space is cleared, the energy of freed-up space feels like another burden has been lifted!**

In light of these thoughts, have a look at your bedroom and try to be objective if you can. *Is it cluttered? Are your closets too full? Are countertops covered with too many items? Are you storing boxes beneath your bed or elsewhere? Do you remember what's in those boxes? Could their contents be better used by someone else, perhaps?*

Energy needs to flow freely throughout your home — this is a basic Feng Shui principle — and especially in the bedroom where you spend several hours each night breathing in the air as you sleep. Congested areas in bedrooms are not conducive to freely moving, fresh air!

Donate the items you no longer use to support your favourite charity, and **allow air and energy to flow into these former congested areas**, to lighten up the spaces throughout your home. **Remembering that Reiki is energy, this is all a part of a Self-Care Reiki lifestyle.** Decluttering also includes removing or reducing the amount of electrical equipment from the bedroom such as a TV, computer, play station, etc.

Still in the bedroom, *What about your lighting, your colour scheme, and your bedding? Is it all to your personal comfort? Does it make you feel good when you walk into your bedroom?* You could consider repainting the bedroom with a calming elemental colour that is inviting easy sleep and bedding that supports this invitation, plus a bedside lamp for relaxing reading to stimulate sleep. And open those windows to allow fresh air entry from outdoors.

Reflection

Consider what, if any, decluttering of your lifestyle may be necessary at this point in your life.

Here is a simple energy trick I like to use when I am trying to be objective. I close my eyes and imagine myself floating above the situation, then looking down from above it to 'see' it differently in my mind as to how it affects me energetically.

Perhaps you'd like to try this by floating above each room in your home and look down on it in this way. As you do this, notice how it makes you feel …

It's simple to do and often quite revealing. You can use this method to check on other activities also if you are feeling like other parts of your life may be too cluttered. Often, you already know the answer, yet have not found a way to correct or resolve your situation. Maybe this exercise will help you see beyond what is possible when you are not immersed within it.

Have your journal beside you as you reflect upon all of this, to record what you notice and how you feel energetically as you consider various aspects of your life … at the very least, this exercise will make you more aware of how you interact with energy forces in your life … for each activity has an energy associated with it. You interact with the energy consciously or unconsciously. It is either draining you or filling you up. It's important to know the difference!

Medicate or Meditate?

Many people rely on medication for sleep. In light of all we have discussed so far, let's turn now to the non-medication assists for sleep. Begin about a half hour before bedtime to purposely slow down ... do your bedtime rituals of getting ready for bed, then purposely spend some time away from the television, your phone or computer ... perhaps listen to some relaxing music with your hands against your chest and feel yourself begin to relax before you go to bed. The exercise we tried at the beginning of this chapter is an example of something you might try. And combine it with your gratitude practice by using this time to go over the highlights of your day that were positive and allow this energy of gratitude to flow within you, **consciously giving thanks for your day and for the night that is upon you** *in the presence of now* **... allowing all of these thoughts to settle in this space to be acknowledged** *before going to bed*. And then when you are ready to crawl into bed, here are a number of suggestions for hand positions you might use when you are ready to turn out the light and drift off to sleep.

Position One

You may recall in our last session, I asked you to **place your hands – one above the other – touching your Right thumb-tip and first finger-tip to the bony edges of your Left wrist, then rest your hands comfortably along the midline of your body.** This position can also be done lying on your back or on your side.

Note: You may wish to use the Left thumb and first finger tips against the Right wrist, if it is more comfortable for you.

This is the first position I am suggesting for you to try because it is so simple and because it usually works. Of interest, in heart meridian massage terminology, this is also the general location of the 'Spirit Gate,'[36] used to calm the spirit and help with insomnia. Although the touch points are not identical, it would appear that the results are similar.

Please lie down now to try this position before continuing, allowing your body to relax into the position. Remember to be conscious of your breath and breathe more slowly ...

You could add to this, the touching of your large toes, if you are on your back, an activity that is more easily accomplished when your feet are beneath the sheets.

In general, this position stimulates the ether element in your body, and can bring a sense of calming when you need it and therefore, it may help you settle for sleep. It can also be used in times of stress. It can be even be done quite subtly when you are in a meeting or when you feel a need to de-stress. Remember to breathe more slowly and completely a few times, to help to still your mind and train it to relax!

Position Two

Let's move on now to a variation of three positions which you have previously tried sitting up. This time, try them lying down.

Please lie on your back with a light cover; open your legs slightly and allow your toes to point inwards so that your large toes are touching, if this is comfortable ... otherwise, allow your feet to fall out to the side, away from each other ... then place your hands comfortably on either side of your chest, fingers pointed in towards your heart centre, then take several slower and deeper breaths, becoming aware of consciously relaxing muscles in your body beginning with your head, then slowly moving your conscious awareness downwards in your body all the way to your feet ... while imagining that your body is warming and relaxing as you focus on each area ... breathing more slowly as you progress.

In this position, you might also try resting your finger tips against the underside of your collar bones on either side of your chest, with elbows bent and relaxed, lying alongside your body. This is another Ether Element position as is position one, above. And each position as you will note, uses your finger tips.

Position Three

Still lying on your back, move your hands to your solar plexus ... resting your palms along the underside of your rib cage, middle finger tips touching or almost touching ... take another full breath here and relax into the healing space of warmth beneath your hands. Let your arms comfortably support your hands in the area beneath your ribs just above your navel ... notice how this feels ... In this position, your toes can be touching also, if this is comfortable and relaxing.

Focus on the feeling of your hands against your body and allow this to become your only thought, noticing the warmth and the connection of hands to torso ... imagining your hands melting into your body becoming one with your torso with no separation ... feeling fully connected ... body ... mind ... spirit and soul ...

Begin counting backwards slowly, from ten, taking a long and slow breath between each number.

Position Four

And now, still lying on your back, please move the palm of your right hand to beneath the back of your neck and place the palm of your left hand gently over your sacral chakra, between the bony edges of your pelvis and above the pubic bone ... breathe slowly and deeply in this position ... consciously relaxing your arms and shoulders as your right hand finds comfort beneath your neck ... palm directly beneath the centre of your neck ... breathe your energy downwards now through your chest and torso, your pelvis, into your hips and thighs ... your knees ... lower legs ... feet ... and toes ... if you've been able to let your large toes touch, they will likely be feeling quite warm by now ... helping draw your energy downwards such that Reiki is flowing throughout you now ... welcome this with your breath ... consciously notice the sensation of your hands on your body ... and noticing when you cannot feel them anymore (in any of our sleep positions) ... as though there is no separation of body parts or mind ... you are whole ... together ... fluid ... one ... and soon, perhaps ... asleep!

Position Five

Our final position is turning on to your favourite side, and crossing your arms to hold the space inside your shoulders ... so that your left hand is just inside your right shoulder beside your neck, and your right hand is just inside your left shoulder, on the other side of your neck. If you are on your left side, then bend your right knee and move this leg up as far as you can to be comfortable. Similarly, if you are on your right side, bend you left knee and move your left leg into a supportive and comfortable position. Then just breathe more slowly, aware of the comfort of this position ... in the presence of now ... in this position you are stimulating meridian flow in the body that begins in this upper region.

Note: These positions can all be done in succession, if you wish a longer form of self-care at bedtime, or just do one position on any given night. Eventually, you will find that you naturally place your hands on your body every night without even thinking about it. **Your hands will guide you to the location on your body that needs the additional energy, or that knows its way to sleep!** Do not be surprised if you are placing your hands on this same location for months at a time, as your body feeds its depleted self with needed energy.

And as part of this commentary, I am moved to say, **"Congratulations!"** ... **for taking the steps you are taking to care for yourself energetically.** You are most definitely finding your way back to your 'inner home' we spoke about many chapters ago. *Keep going ... the light can be seen shining in the window of your inner home space now ... rejoicing ... and happily waiting for you to fully return!*

Bottom Line Teaching

A Self-Care Reiki practice trains us to live in a 'presence of now' reality, even at bedtime, such that we can use our hands and our breath to relax our body /mind to settle into a peaceful healing space of much deserved sleep.

I'll leave you now to rest a little longer and perhaps you might try one of these positions tonight and see if it is a good fit for you.

Bedtime Meditation

As we have already said, Self-Care Reiki gentle hands-on touch, done in a peaceful setting of relaxation, is a form of meditation. Bedtime affords a perfect opportunity to experience this. The preceding positions, therefore, are each an opportunity for meditation at the end of your day that may lead you into sleep, the best form of meditation, according to Dalai Lama. Learn which, if any, of these positions brings a sense of stillness to you before you go to sleep, and allows you to drop off to sleep more easily, or to return to sleep if you wake up in the night.

Each of the positions can be done with quiet music playing at the same time, or in silence. Insight Timer has a number of sleep meditations you can try to help you relax at bedtime and get a better night's sleep, one of which is my own, called 'Reiki Meditation for a Peaceful Sleep.' [37] There is no cost for this meditation or for the App.

In our next session we will look at Self-Care Reiki from the perspective of healing root causes that prevent peace and sleep. In the meantime, please be gentle with yourself ... I hope you will sleep well tonight, remembering to be grateful for a good night's sleep ... *before* you go to sleep! Namaste!

CHAPTER NINE

Resolving Root Causes of Obstacles to Create Peace

A Self-Care Reiki practice trains us to live in a 'presence of now' reality, where peace can be found and felt amidst chaos; where lives can be lived from our inner home of peace, and where peace can be shared in all that we do and are.

Reiki will always go to the root cause of symptoms through its energy-healing capability. Much of the time we do not know what is at the bottom of a problem, and yet the healing energy will go to this place through a self-care practice, and resurrect energies that may have created a lifetime of imbalance and disharmony. It may take years to unearth deeply rooted wounds. With each removal, there will be a time of healing awareness and presence of now opportunity for choice to release. As we become more adept at recognizing these times in our healing journey, we become more efficient in surrendering to the wisdom of Reiki healing and its timetable. **Over time, our Self-Care Reiki practice *as lifestyle,* will reward us by leading us to our inner home of authenticity, wherein lies inner peace.** This session begins and ends with a guided Self-Care Reiki Meditation of relaxation and healing.

The pathway to inner peace is fraught with hills and valleys,
echoing the words of your thoughts,
Am I there yet?

Welcome back. Make yourself comfortable within your physical home space, lighting your candle, pausing and centering with Gassho, and playing some quiet meditative music to help you relax into today's reading retreat! My soothing and beautiful sound healing listening suggestion today is called 'The Peaceful Heart,'[38] and can be found on Insight Timer.

To begin today's session, we're going to use our Self-Care Reiki finger tips against the midline of our body, front and back in a centering exercise. I'd like you to place your right hand on the back of your head such that your finger tips can rest vertically along the midline of your head with your second and third fingers resting **very gently** against the centre of the back of your neck, just beneath the bony base of your skull. You may need to support your right elbow on the back of your chair if you are sitting up, or on your pillow if you are lying down. Then, place your other hand on the front of your body, with your left finger tips resting vertically on the midline of your body's core ... anywhere this feels comfortable – second, third, fourth or fifth chakra. Then relax comfortably into this very gentle Self-Care Reiki touch position making any adjustment you may need to be comfortable, while listening to the music and breathing more slowly. You may wish to put your book or tablet down to just enjoy this position for a few moments before reading further.

Reflection

Can you describe your experience now in words in your journal?

In today's session, we'll continue with our earlier theme of 'being held,' as we look at obstacles to inner peace. Essentially, healing is possible within the context of the Ether Element — *where, theoretically, healing universal energies of nature meet and 'hold us.'* Often, it will be in a natural setting that something will surface in your more peaceful mind, directing your attention to the need to reach out to someone, to acknowledge or to forgive, for example.

I hope you were able to experience the Ether Element in our opening exercise today, even for a moment. As a quick review, the Ether Element in nature makes itself known to us in very practical ways, where each of the elements is present. Spending time in nature is always a healing space, even if you are oblivious to 'her' beauty. **By stopping to sense and feel her beauty, you are welcoming this energy of nature into your body, to heal you on deeper levels.**

In energy-healing, it is not simply one's symptoms being treated; the energy is always going to the source or root cause of one's symptoms. This point is very important in understanding Reiki. **Reiki is essentially an interactive form of self-care healing. As you consciously treat a symptom, you are actually treating the cause which will likely require an investment in time.** With perseverance in Self-Care Reiki you may find that you are guided to do something about the cause — which may be unknown to you, consciously, *as cause.* (This is the interactive part.)

As mentioned above, sometimes it will be in nature that you will receive an idea to do something which could lead you to the cause or source of your symptoms. It may be a need to forgive someone ... or yourself ... for something that happened a long time ago. In those fresh, presence-of-now-moments of insight, it will become clear for you that you need to do something (although you may not realize why.)

The second aspect of Reiki's interactive requirement then, is for you to take action once you feel moved to take action! At some point later, you may discover that the symptom you have experienced for some time is no longer present. (And yet, you may not link these two occurrences.) This is the journey of Self-Care Reiki! **Reiki's energy is always going to the cause of your discontent, whatever that may be.** I might add here, that this is one of the main reasons Reiki research is so challenging; it is impossible to prove the direct causal link to healing. It is only with the passage of time that you will notice a symptom is no longer present ... perhaps coincidentally, you may discover that your anger over an incident many years ago is no longer as issue. *Were these two pieces of information linked? And even if they may have been, how can you prove it scientifically?*

The only scientific data that can support a Reiki practice, in general, is the ability to measure the effect of the relaxation or parasympathetic response derived through the relaxation benefits of Reiki energy. Clinically, The Mayo Clinic supports the use of 'relaxation techniques' to reduce stress, citing benefits such as: a decreased heart rate, decreased blood pressure and slower breathing, maintaining blood sugar levels, reducing activity of stress hormones, improved digestion, maintaining blood flow to major muscles, improving sleep quality, reducing anger and frustration.[39]

In a recent article, psychologist Dr. Arielle Schwartz, in reference to body movement, especially yoga, says:

"The use of mind-body therapies ... can help you access the nourishing benefits of your parasympathetic nervous system. These restorative practices can help you improve digestion, increase immune system functioning, enhance thyroid health, and improve symptoms of depression."[40]

When we use our Self-Care Reiki practice such as we have already discussed in this book — *connecting to the environment in our mind as we walk outdoors with awareness of the earth beneath our feet and the sensation of 'being held' by the combination of natural elements in the presence of now (i.e. truly focused on all of this), and in gratitude for every living thing* — we are accomplishing what each of these articles supports. Or, if we sit in the stillness of Reiki Meditation, using self-care touch, we are stimulating Reiki energy flow in our body, and the subsequent Relaxation Response, deriving body / mind relaxation and a shift in our emotional state of peacefulness.

Finally, when one is mindfully committed to healing through self-care, **the use of gentle touch plus the Precepts engages all systems — the mental, emotional and physical ... all impacting the spiritual aspect of your being, leading you to your inner home of peace and authenticity.** With this complete level of engagement, a Self-Care Reiki practice becomes 'lifestyle,' a healing lifestyle.

Many of our root causes of imbalance are based in our emotional selves and are experienced in various parts of our bodies. When I see a hospice family member for a Reiki session, I always take a few moments before having them lie down on the table, to create a safe and healing environment for them. During this time, I ask if they have had Reiki previously. Most have never even heard of it. In all cases, they want to know what it will do to them, *or for them.* I cannot answer this question, of course, since each of us is different. Each one of us is carrying our own burdens, wearing them uniquely within our bodies. Because of this, the way each person reacts to the session is completely out of my control. All I can honestly tell them, is that they will probably feel more relaxed afterwards. As practitioner, I am not 'a healer,' as some energy workers would call themselves, **I am simply 'a channel' through which healing energy flows.**

This same understanding applies to a self-care practice of Reiki also. It is impossible to determine how your energy-healing journey will unfold. A daily Self-Care Reiki Meditation practice and use of the Precepts will raise up various energies, like removing the branches from your inner stream, we spoke about in our third chapter on the water element.

With each 'branch removal,' or release of congested energy, your inner stream of energy is able to move more freely. This becomes more important as we consider our relaxation response and the ability for Reiki to reduce blood pressure, for example. Perhaps it is because of all those branches that blood pressure becomes a concern. *What else might become a concern?*

By engaging in your Self-Care Reiki Meditation practice with an intent to heal, and with no other intentional parameters than this, the healing energy of the Universe will dislodge each of those metaphoric branches along your inner stream, carefully removing them, one by one in 'divine time,' engaging your interactive assistance, as necessary, to be released. Sometimes, branches are laden with other debris that must be released also, before being able to get to smaller branches trapped beneath.

Some of the debris may be recognizable to you, having memories that surface for you to examine prior to its removal. Some people, at this stage of healing, cannot face their self-created debris, or their responsibility for it and so they remain where they are. *What happens to blood pressure (and other) implications now?* **Will these branches remain an obstacle to inner peace?**

Or, the cause of the debris may be tied to the need to forgive. It continues to live on needlessly, since the person is unwilling to forgive, or to acknowledge that they, themselves, may have been wrong in actions taken a long time ago. **(Another obstacle to inner peace and another potential health implication.)**

And sometimes there are many small branches that bear a resemblance to one another, creating a sense that as one is released, they all are ... only to find another aspect of the same issue coming up again and again. When you consider each issue as a branch within a stack of similar branches, you can understand why we seem to always be working on the same issue in our personal healing and growth. This causes some to give up on this natural course of inner healing, suggesting it doesn't work! **... another obstacle to inner peace.**

In time, however, with our daily Self-Care Reiki practice, even our aligned stacks of branches can be separated out and released also, freeing us from that burden that prevents our inner elemental energy flow of peace. So the message here is obvious: **keep up your Self-Care Reiki practice!**

The road to inner peace cannot be expected to be easy if you have never been able to feel peace! Rest assured, it is there ... *inside of you* ... waiting patiently for your return home! Listen to those sources of insight that flow at the most unexpected times ... follow through on what it is you are moved to do ... trust in the process ...

Feeling moved to do something is the intuitive part of your healing journey ... awakening you into action (with potential results) for you ... *and you will know by your actions, you will know, you will know ... Reiki energy is love ... you will know, you will know ...*

Sometimes the key to your own healing is your awareness and willingness to remove the branches. For example:

- You can choose to forgive, or not forgive ... *are you ready to forgive?*
- You can choose to stop addictive habits or not ... *are you ready to give them up?*
- You can choose to continue your search for your inner truth, or you can give up ... *are you ready to uncover your inner truth and authenticity?*
- You can choose to continue your search for inner peace or not ... *are you ready to continue the search?*

In each case, we encounter interactive Reiki ... we have a choice, as to whether our branch debris can be released.

The more we align ourselves with the positive space of healing energy that we visit during Self-Care Reiki Meditation, the more easily all of this happens. Our choices become clear! *The results?*

Our body and mind are positively affected by the energy of our action and healing happens that is beyond our control and beyond our awareness ... we find ourselves one day simply feeling differently and better ... perhaps not even realizing what it is that has changed. You will just know that it feels like you are in a secure and beautiful space ... *this is the space of your authentic self ... your inner home ... the space of peace.* In metaphoric terms, the branches have been removed from our internal stream and our inner waterway flows freely once again.

When the soul feels confidently 'held' within the Universal energies of the natural elements, healing happens that is beyond the conscious body / mind. You may feel a sense of calm where once there was anxiety ... a peaceful, quiet inner stillness that was not there before. Or you may feel a surge of excitement, knowing you are indeed connected to this invisible healing space of the Universe that is holding you at this very moment ... *in the living presence of now!*

This is the healing space of enlightened awareness that Reiki's founder, Mikao Usui, referred to as *Anshin Ritsumei*, meaning the place of inner peace amidst chaos. In other words, we cannot change the world around us, we can only change the world *within* us ... from moment to moment, in the presence of now, **we can choose to change how we react to the chaos of the world around us ... some, of which, we may have created!**

This is what Usui Sensi delivered to us through such a simple practice he called Reiki ... where all we need to do is place our hands upon our body and welcome healing energy ... then surrender ourselves, meditatively, to 'be held' by the loving Universe *in the presence of now ... through our willingness to receive the universal comforts of caring, compassion and love ... all translated to us as feelings of peace.*

This is the healing space of authentic peace that people attempt to explain following a Reiki session with a Reiki practitioner, yet, they cannot, because it is so foreign to them. They have forgotten this sensation of absolute peace ... this 'inner home' space of their spirit ... this sense of 'something more' that some would call *pure consciousness*, Divine or higher intelligence. Still others, in their complete respect for it, cannot begin to assign it a word ... *it just is* ... and in that moment of acknowledgement ... *of inner wisdom* ... the Universe, with all of its mystical questions begins to make sense ... *in the pure and simple feeling of the Divine presence of now ...*

In this magical healing space of peace, our emotional energy imbalances that have created fear within us are soothed, if not reduced. And with continued attention via a Self-Care Reiki practice, **the root cause of our imbalance *can* be eliminated! The final branch of a long-held issue can be removed from our internal stream forever, and our inner waters can flow again in ways previously forgotten.**

What recipients of a full Reiki session with a practitioner *can* report, is an ability to breathe effortlessly and exhale fully, as though they've been holding their breath previously ... unable to exhale. The world looks differently to them afterwards — like the woman I described in an earlier chapter who reported seeing the wild flowers growing by the roadside on her way home following her first Reiki attunement. She was opened and introduced, through her attunement, to a level of being and awareness that her soul had been searching to find. This was made evident through her sudden awareness of seeing flowers for the very first time, although they had always been there.

The consequence of forgetting is many of the things that Usui Sensei deemed were essential to live a full life — *like the ability to stop worrying, to stop breeding anger, to live an honest and truthful life, to show compassion to ourselves and others as we honour our parents, teachers and elders, and to be grateful for every living thing.* The Reiki Precepts counteract these energies of dysfunction, by mindfully guiding people back to their inner home where they can truly find relief from constant anxiety, and experience the healing space of authentic peace.

Many of us have forgotten what we are searching for ... this inner home of peace ... for life has moved us so far from our inner home. In times like the Covid — 19 Pandemic, perhaps this has been a perfect opportunity to return to our basic values and resume the search. Clearly, it is in a Self-Care Reiki practice of meditation and energy healing that we are returned to this authentic aspect of ourselves once again ... amidst any crisis, *in the healing presence of now.*

Having found our inner home space again, we can remain in this healing space through our continued daily practice of Self-Care Reiki Meditation, where we simply place our hands upon our body in the space that we recognize is needing to be touched — then relax into this space and allow ourselves to experience the comfort of inner quiet. Such a practice prevents the addition of branches and debris in our inner stream; it keeps us fully conscious of the healing space we are in and that we automatically share with others, without even trying.

Bottom Line Teaching

A Self-Care Reiki practice trains us to live in a 'presence of now' reality, where peace can be found and felt amidst chaos; where lives can be lived from our inner home of peace and where peace can be shared in all that we do and are.

Closing Reiki Meditation

Note: Remember, you can record this meditation to truly relax and benefit from its potential healing effect.

Quite often it is our heart space that will lead us to our inner quiet — **please move your hands now to your heart centre ... perhaps you could also try bringing the soles of your feet together if this is possible for you** ... you have energy centres on the soles of your feet that can be utilized in restoring energy. **When both your hands and your feet are engaged in self-care touch, your body energy flow becomes one continuous circuit of energy.** (This is helpful for the condition of neuropathy of the feet.) If you cannot do this position comfortably, then place your feet flat on the floor and imagine you are drawing healing earth energy upwards into your body as we continue ...

Once settled, begin to take slower and deeper breaths ... allowing yourself to feel your hands .... and your feet ... their warmth ... and their comfort ... allowing yourself to completely relax as you take another deeper breath ... then giving yourself over to the idea of 'being held' in this position now ... by your own warm hands against your chest ... then breathe this warmth slowly ... with each breath a little deeper ... your entire body relaxing more with each breath ... as you move, deeper still ... into the space where healing energies meet ... restoring you in peace ... reassuring you of 'something more' ... something more that lives within you ... constant ... soothing ... eternal ... yours ... enough ... your inner home ... the healing space where you may always return for comfort ... love ... and peace ...your inner home of peace ...

> As you continue to relax into the healing space of
> peace ... allow your body, mind, spirit and soul to
> be united in this sense of peace ... no longer feeling
> your hands as they melt into an awareness of being
> one with the rest of your body ... one with your
> mind ... one with your spirit and soul ... rest and
> float in this healing space for as long as feels com-
> fortable for you ... dropping off to sleep possibly ...
> allowing yourself to be held and healed by the living
> presence of now, the life-giving, restorative energy
> of the Universe.

Remain here in this position for as long as you can spend today, as you remind yourself to be gentle with yourself.

Namaste!

Afterwards ...

Sometimes, our healing journey feels like we are 'stuck' and we are not sure why. When this happens and we look for answers (the interactive part of Reiki), **quite often the Universe will reflect a healing space to us that will capture our attention.** This could be as simple as a friend quite innocently telling you something 'apparently unrelated,' that sheds light on the cause of your being stuck. Or, you may receive insight through meditation, or a dream, that speaks to your issue. Or you may receive the suggestion of a book to read only to discover that it holds a key for your understanding to move forward. Or, you may feel drawn to go on retreat or a holiday, where you can have time in a healing environment ... and an answer will come to you. And sometimes, you may feel called to spend time in a place of your youth, to relive memories that need to be revisited to render you 'unstuck.'

Any of these activities and countless more, can represent a healing space for you where you can experience a deep sense of inner peace. This is important, because if you find yourself struggling and an invitation comes along that may seem outside your comfort zone — yet a safe place to be — it may be an opportunity being offered by the Universe, through a friend or an add, etc., to help you become 'unstuck' and move you out of your rut and into a new 'home-space' of comfort unknown to you before. *This is another example of how the Universe holds us!*

You may also meet this healing space during your practice of Self-Care Reiki. And when you do, you can readily acknowledge that there is 'something more' to your life ... **something more that can lift depression, that can stimulate and reassure, restore confidence, excite and relax all at the same time.**

Literally every person in the world during the Covid-19 Pandemic has been given an opportunity to test this theory of getting caught up within the chaos or choosing to remain calm so as to find an awakened sense of peaceful strength *within,* to cope amidst the chaos.

We can truly acknowledge this inner space of healing through the lens of our authentic selves. **Living a life of truth naturally guides us along our inner path to find the healing space of peace that each of us craves.**

Some believe that this is only possible in death, as we read in obituaries that speak to a peaceful death following months or years of suffering. And although, death can be reached in peace, Usui Sensei was speaking to something that is possible in the world of the living, long before the time of death. His sense of Anshin Ritsumei, I suspect, was a goal for any of us to reach ... a reward for surrendering to 'something more' ... and to be guided to this space of peace *within* us.

'Listen' as your Self-Care Reiki practice …
Listen to nature's extraordinary beauty,
'Heard'
through all your senses,
Comforted
through your feelings,
Interpreted as
Music …
Singing directly
to your heart and soul
In familiar notes of Peace …
And welcoming 'sounds' of Home.

CHAPTER TEN

The Healing Space of Now

A Self-Care Reiki practice trains us to live in the feelings of a 'presence of now' reality, where each of our energy centres flow freely with the comforts of love and peace.

In these last nine chapters, we have covered what I consider to be the most important teachings of Reiki for day-today living in terms of self care. So, **thank you for reading this far and considering these teachings to make a difference in your life.** Reiki, as a healing practice for oneself and for others, has spread all over the world. It may be taught differently, as one might expect; however, the essence that makes Reiki special remains the same, for it is the energy of the Universe. We meet this energy in meditation also. As you have read, Reiki teaches us additional ways to bring this energy into our lives in a moment-to-moment way of being. When we do this for ourselves, we move closer to our potential for harmony and balance, such that we can find our pure sense of authenticity. It is in living our truth that we will come to release that which creates distress and is untrue within us. **Our truth will guide us to experience inner peace in the inner home of our authentic self, *the ultimate goal of Self-Care Reiki.***

Because:

*"Many people live in anxiety, anger, grief and depression —
especially when they face their own suffering and illness."*[41]
— Dr. Xiaolan Zhao, CMD

Please:

*Focus your attention on your Reiki hands
resting on your body as you breathe …
This is learning to focus on 'the presence of now.'
As you develop this sense of the presence of now,
The world will open up to you in new ways …
One moment at a time …
You will see things you've never noticed before …
You will respond in new ways …
You will live your life in new ways …
You will push your suffering ways to the background …
Determined and grateful
To live the presence of now.*

We meet 'the presence of now'
in healing spaces within nature all the time ...
the healing part comes to us when we gift
ourselves with the space of time
to stop ... here ... and meet the healing space of now ...
where the language of inner knowing
is revealed ...

Memories flourish as I recall a summer holiday with my parents around the age of twelve. Our motel faced a lake that was active with boats and wave action in the evening prior to going to bed. In the morning, the lake was completely transformed. It was like glass ... the morning stillness was palpable in the moist air rising from the lake ... in the warmth of the rising sun ... in the complete absence of activity or human sound ... yet, it was more than this for me, although this certainly set the stage for the sense I feel even now as I remember this simple scene ... *it was the strong and alive sense of the feeling of now!* And in this moment of recall, I also sense what I now know to be root chakra energy combined with the energy of all the elements, for in this location each element was present, creating the opportunity for healing ... I was a kid, mature for my age ... a kid nonetheless, and carefree ... no worries ... cared for and about ... protected and loved ... in that critical moment before the busyness of our day began, *I felt the precious presence of now in that healing space of morning* ... I instantly understood, somehow, the silent language of 'inner knowing' ... a moment I carry with me still ... **its simplicity, the likes of which, seems to escape us as we grow into our adult life, filled with responsibility** ... *in the chosen absence of time and space ... the absence of the healing presence of now ... the absence of here!*

Hello again,

It's time to light your candle one last time of sharing our heal-ing space together. Perhaps this time, as you experience the peaceful glow of candlelight in Gassho position, you could give thanks not only for healing you have experienced along our way together, please give thanks for healing that is already occurring as you continue on in your self-care journey ... keeping the momentum of healing active in your body / mind. Then close your eyes for a centering moment ...

We'll begin this last chapter with some review before finding a few more ways of describing Reiki to you. But first ...

Please turn on your quiet meditation music and feel your body instinctively receiving the cues for relaxation ... today, I am suggesting you might try a cello meditation[42] from Insight Timer ... then, take a moment to notice how you are feeling today ... if you have discomfort in some part of your body place your hands there. Or perhaps you would pre-fer to place your hands in one of the positions we have discussed already, especially if it seemed to bring comfort to you. Then slow your breath ... and settle in comfortably to meditate ... And this time, I would like you to keep your eyes open as you relax into your position of comfort, and look around you in your own place of home ... your external healing space of home — your external space of *here.* I trust that in this space you have found a way to make it feel like a retreat space that is comforting to you and that you are finding yourself wanting to spend more time *here. Relax now into your home space of here ...*

in this healing space of now ... living it ... breathing it ...enjoying it ... feeling gratitude for it ... enjoying the warmth of your hands resting gently on your body ... being excessively gentle with yourself ... and smile ...

Reflection

* Please reflect back on your reading thus far, and record in your journal those things that have stood out for you, and which you are already doing as part of your self-care practice.

* Please record the positions of gentle touch you find the most comforting, and are using. These may change as you continue your self-care practice.

* Please also record which of the Precepts you find yourself thinking about and using by incorporating them in some way into your life. This is a topic you may wish to expand upon at another time as well.

Being in the Self-Care Reiki Flow

As you've begun to realize, in its truest sense, Reiki is well beyond physical touch or even explanation. How I express Reiki in this book will not be identical to how another author expresses it. The energy of Reiki presents itself to me in the ways I have shared with you, as it flows through my life experience. Reiki flows through the life experience of others, and through your life experience also.

This is one of the unique beauties of Reiki as a self-care practice. **Reiki meets you exactly where you are — just like the sun shining on the water** — and journeys with you through all of your life experience, like a friend who will always be there for you, guiding your way home ... to your 'inner home' ... the home space inside of you where a light quietly burns in the window, welcoming you with love and compassion on your safe return.

Gentle, hands-on touch is the daily touchstone of a Self-Care Reiki practice which, over time, grooms us to be our authentic selves .... to feel comfortable in our own skin and understand what this means and feels like ... it is a subtle, yet expansive energy that returns us to our presence of now ... whatever this may be ...

A Self-Care Reiki practice sets us on a journey of healing those aspects of ourselves that are not aligned with our authentic self. What this means is that as we continue to administer Self-Care Reiki to ourselves, we begin to change in ways we hardly notice until one day we realize that something feels different and more comfortable.

Along the way to get to this healing space, you may find you have days where you feel lower energy. This is normal. These are the days to make sure you are continuing your practice of Self-Care Reiki, to keep the flow of healing energy moving in your body. *Remember that Reiki energy is doing its work within your daily practice, to clear away the debris in your internal stream and to prevent more debris from building up.* *

It is so important to continue with your hands-on practice at this point and with the affirmations of the Precepts. One day you will notice a difference that assures you that you are clearing your own energy flow in this way. I should mention also, that some of this debris may be unknown to you, perhaps because it is not a part of this lifetime. But this is another subject outside our topic.

* (I like to use this metaphor of the stream, because it is so easy to picture in your mind.)

You can combine your Self-Care Reiki energy-awareness practice with exercise in nature, such as jogging, walking and golfing. As you jog, walk or golf, etc., remain aware of your surroundings in nature, of the beauty that surrounds you; then breathe in the beauty, aligning with its energy as you exercise. **Your conscious awareness of beauty in nature aligns you with the spiritual side of nature, of 'something more' in the Universe, and of the energy you feel in your body, or the presence of now as you are outdoors enjoying it ... breathing its healing energy as you exercise.**

Regular exercise is crucial for your health, as is the food you eat; remember to make good nutritional choices for a well-balanced diet. A Self-Care Reiki practice may even guide you to make better choices in each of these areas.

Are you in the Reiki Flow or The Worry Flow?

As I now say to my students, "You can be in the worry flow or the Reiki flow, the anger flow or the Reiki, flow, etc." Think about this when something interrupts a good day. *How do you choose to react?* **Remaining in the Reiki flow is where you begin to heal.**

Usui Sensei only mentioned two common emotions of anger and worry that throw us off balance. I suspect that his intention was for people to use their common sense to create additional, relevant Precepts for themselves to deal with other emotions too, like fear, jealousy, frustration, critical judgement, etc., to name only a few.

Deep within us all lies fear that rises up in forms that we do not associate as fear ... as examples:

* fear is at the base of worry,
* fear can trigger an unease that leads to anger,
* fear can prevent us from seeing the good in others; instead, we may feel suspicion, jealousy or resentment,
* fear is the obstacle that keeps us from knowing our inner truth; authenticity is not fear, it is Divine,
* fear keeps us from knowing peace,
* fear keeps us constantly on edge, needing weapons to protect us rather than love and goodwill,
* fear is at the base of much, if not most, dysfunction in the world,
* fear is the mesh that holds dysfunctional energies in place,
* fear is usually the final energy of dysfunction we release, to truly know peace.

Looking back over the healing Precepts or affirmations we have discussed, **we have found ways to replace fear at the**

source of worry, of our ability to trust, and of finding comfort in our own truth and authenticity. **We've done this using fear's antithesis — love, and peace.**

Noticing which energy 'flow' you are in, is about taking responsibility for your own behaviour and actions. *Are you in the Reiki flow of love and peace, or are you in the jealous or resentful flow of dysfunctional energy, which can create anxiety and insecurity?*

Becoming aware of *how you are truly feeling* **in any given moment ...** *in the presence of now* **... highlights whether or not you are in the Reiki flow!** If you are not in the Reiki flow, you are offered a Self-Care Reiki question: *Do I want to remain in my own negativity or do I want to to move back into my Reiki flow again, where everything feels better than I feel right now? Or, do I want or need to continue to feel hurt and blame?*

As we progress on our life's journey, we discover how important it is that we take responsibility for our life, our health being a very important aspect of our life. Self-Care Reiki, is a huge step to take on your journey of responsibility, as you learn to let go of energies that harm you and others, and prevent you from living your life to the fullest, in good health. Learning to be grateful for all that you are will make a difference in your life, and in the lives of those you touch each day *with your presence.*

Self-Care Reiki turns the responsibility for your own wellbeing to you! It is not another voice making suggestions to you as to how you 'should' be living your life.

You are always in control of your own actions ... you are always in control as to whether to get back into the Reiki flow or to watch your life from the sidelines and not engage with the possibilities that exist if you decide to re-engage.

It's very simple to re-engage ... you have to be willing to give up your feelings of angst towards someone or even towards yourself in relation to something that has upset you. In short, you have to let go of anger ... or jealousy ... or resentment, shame, or ego, etc. It actually takes less energy to re-engage in the Reiki flow than to continue to hold on to the energies of dysfunction that keep you outside the flow! It feels a lot better also, to return to the Reiki flow!

The basic Precepts that form the mindfulness aspect of Self-Care Reiki were created with *you* in mind, and with *me* in mind ... not in name, *in principle.* If we insist upon holding on to anger and fear and guilt, to name just a few of life's personal growth inhibitors, we remain outside our 'inner home' ... never to know its comforts ... never to know its peace.

At any time you can calm yourself within a deep Self-Care Reiki breath of peace.

In those times, simply return to the space you are sitting in right now ... light your candle, use the Gassho technique of centering and take a deep breath of peace. Then place your hands over your heart centre and close your eyes and take another deep Self-Care Reiki breath of peace ... with complete awareness that you are choosing to return to the Reiki flow ... then remain there in your special space ... your retreat space ... your *sacred space* for self-care healing energy ... until you feel better again ... sensing your body and mind relaxing ... and your 'Reiki flow' returning ...

If this doesn't work for you, then go outdoors into a favourite location in nature to find stillness and spend time there ...

Allow yourself to be comforted by the environment. Breathe in the trees ... the earth ... the sky ... the moisture in the air or the beauty of water, if present, the sunshine filtering through leaves ... sit down on a rock or a tree stump, or on the ground ... look around you and give thanks for this healing space ... allow yourself to be comforted by this healing space ... remain until you begin to feel your Reiki flow returning as your upset is neutralized by the space where all the healing elements meet ... and give thanks again ...

Sometimes, we need to go through this progression of energy reactions following some kind of upset that has occurred, to really understand that **we do have the inner control to reverse the initial way we feel following an upset ... to relax back into our true selves again,** with peaceful awareness of who we truly are ... and then to deal with what has happened with a cooler mind and calmer body.

There are many other ways of using Self-Care Reiki to help you return to your more centred way of being. For example, you can:

- walk your Self-Care Reiki practice, taking your Earth Element surroundings into your awareness, breathing gratitude for all that is,

- paint or craft your Self-Care Reiki practice, creatively engaging in your Water Element,

- dance your Self-Care Reiki practice, allowing your Fire Element energy to flow freely, feeling light and joyful,

- breathe your Self-Care Reiki practice, connecting with your inner Air Element,

- meditate your Self-Care Reiki practice using the energies of the Ether Element as you feel your inner sense of stillness and peace,

- sing your Self-Care Reiki practice in gratitude for all that is and for being in all that is ...

- listen as your Self-Care Reiki practice ... listening with ether's intensity of awareness to nature's sounds as 'music of the Universe,' speaking to the heart and soul of those who listen ...

* affirm your Self-Care Reiki practice through the mindful affirmations of the Precepts,

* sit by the bedside of one who is dying, comfortably sharing sacred space together, *feeling the presence of now* as a result of your Self-Care Reiki practice ... or

* smile warmly to a child, and this becomes your light-affirming Self-Care Reiki experience.

You can do any of these things and more,[43] and call them Reiki because Reiki is healing energy that flows easily within you when you open yourself to receive its healing benefits ... Reiki's benefits know no boundary ... Reiki is energy ... its potential is everywhere and in every 'thing!'

Using Reiki as self care becomes a limitless practice. If there is a miracle to be found in Reiki, then perhaps this is it. As a simple mode of self care, it is always available, always pure and reliable and with no expiry date. As we heal and grow within its energy, so does its ability to take us further ... to reveal more energy awareness secrets to us, 'hooking us' by the excitement of just being ourselves ... leaving us liberated and satisfied by this alone ...

When does the Universe reach out to us?

'Listen' as your Self-Care Reiki practice ...
Listen with ether's intensity of awareness to nature's sounds
As music of the Universe,
Speaking to the heart and soul
Of those who listen ...

Like an inner language of knowing — the Universe can reach out to us at any point in our life, and in any way, regardless of where we are or who we are with ... and in that moment of inner knowing, we have a choice of listening and responding, or not. As we practice Self-Care Reiki, we become more sensitive to this inner knowing and trusting in its guidance ... more adept in paying attention and answering ... Reiki prepares us for these healing moments of opening, where healing energies meet — in their own time — allowing us to listen more intensely ... to interpret more precisely ... and to respond more confidently when we are ready ... and through all of this, to release more completely, and to heal more fully.

How can we reach out to the Universe?

You can reach out to the healing energies of the universe anytime in meditation or prayer. These times are obvious. However, *Did you realize that you can also reach out to the Universe to connect at the first sound of crickets in the grass at dusk?*

* *or frogs singing in springtime?*
* *or wind blowing in the trees?*
* *or quiet sounds of a gurgling stream?*
* *or the power of ocean waves pounding against the shoreline?*
* *or raindrops falling on rooftops?*
* *or in the magic of a rainbow following the rain?*
* *or observing a sunrise or sunset, or a full moon rise or set?*
* *or while out jogging?*
* *or ending a yoga class, as examples ...*

Your Self-Care Reiki practice sensitizes you to acknowledge *your* place in the Universe during such times ... opening you ... to receive its healing energy, without labelling this energy as Reiki or Meditation or any other title society has tried to place upon its universal healing potential. No speaking is needed. It is a moment of Divine connection you are feeling with the Universe, in the presence of now ... *the language of inner knowing.*

Then without even trying, **being in the Reiki flow allows this balanced energy to move out from you and through you in all you are and do ... it flows in you** in your workplace, your community, family relationships, in all forms of fellowship, including social media and contacts with all you meet, for *you* **are the product of your energy-healing practice of Reiki!**

You can meet any challenge that is before you with peace and authenticity. Remember this! Your inner stillness is what will allow this to happen. You will know this is real when you feel it without trying to understand it. *It just is ... your inner language of knowing ...*

What prevents any of us from doing this? At the root of much of our energy imbalance is both fear and ego.

Let's return our attention one last time to the space where healing energies of the Universe meet ... the space where you consciously feel an invitation from the universe reaching out to be present *to* you and *with* you *in the presence of now* ... it is in this space — this space of *inner knowing* — that Reiki energy arises, and fear and ego can be eradicated such that authenticity and peace can once again flourish.

Such is our Self-Care Reiki practice of energy-healing aware-ness and wellness. Such is our ability to connect with healing energies within ourselves, to become an ego-less healing pres-ence to others in all we do and in all we are. *For*

We are in the mists of time
We are in the silent sounds of waters
We are in the thunderous sounds of oceans
We are in the gentle breezes and the tumultuous hurricanes
We are in all that is.

We find ourselves as we awaken to this level of consciousness:
    of something more,
This level of pure consciousness that acknowledges
This level of pure consciousness that knows ... and understands
That we are in all that is.
Here, healing is in the past.
Healing is in the present, and
Healing will be in the future.
For there will be times when we will forget our past;
There will be times when we will forget
That we are in all that is.

And then, something within this grand spectrum of nature
Will guide us back to the place inside of us that remembers
When time began
And we will once again know that we are in all that is
And that all that is, is within us ...
In the presence of now ...

How can Universal Healing Energy do these things? Here are
my final thoughts:

By recalibrating us to return to our 'inner home' space again,
we 'remember' how to unleash our spirit, and our creative
potential flourishes.

This practice and effect of energy healing is not confined to
Reiki; it is present within all energy healing that connects us to
the space inside of us where healing energies meet, regardless
of where we happen to be or what modality we follow.

Yet, because I am speaking about Reiki in this book, I'll return
to it specifically to continue. The healing result of Reiki energy
is not simply peace and authenticity for the one who has welcomed and received the benefit of Universal Healing Energy.
Its effect is too large to contain within oneself alone. It's like
love ... it spreads out to others through the renewed energy
that we carry within ourselves!

So, we share it in dance, in words, in song, in action, in writ-
ings, in recordings, in wisdom, in stillness, in the workplace, in
our home, in our family, in our community, in social media ...
and throughout our life. It spreads like milk and honey as
needing souls attach to its comfort and take it into their weariness to be renewed also.

Like the expression, "It's everywhere, it's everywhere," this is
Reiki! All we need to do is join its loving flow of healing energy
and wear its healing peace in all of our authentic interactions
with others on any given day of our lives.

Self-Care Reiki is a wonderful tool and way of being to live our life without ego getting in the way and without fear ruining many opportunities we are equipped to meet, that we might grow in our humanness. Self-Care Reiki's effects open us into ever-increasing depths of energy healing and expansiveness in the way we mindfully choose to live our life.

While it is true that Reiki is but one vehicle through which we can arrive in this healing space that understands that we are in all that is, and that all that is, is also in us, it is also true that our Self-Care Reiki vehicle can take us to all the places we need to go within our lifetime and live our life to the fullest.

Anytime *your* Reiki vehicle is running low on gas, simply take it outside for a 'spin' in nature ... where it will fill up naturally with an elementally friendly high octane from the Universe!

Bottom Line Teaching

A Self-Care Reiki practice trains us to live in the feelings of a 'presence of now' reality, where each of our energy centres flow freely with the comforts of love and peace.

As we end our time together, I want to say that **anyone can attend a Reiki class and anyone can practice Reiki on themselves.** It requires no previous experience or education. So if this book has stimulated your interest to go more deeply into a Self-Care Reiki lifestyle, you may wish to attend a first level course in your area, and continue to meet yourself in the ethereal space where healing energies connect and *feel* the presence of *something more* in your life ... *in the presence of now!*

Beyond all these comments though, no one can predict how a Self-Care Reiki practice will affect them. **Only *you* will really know its affects** ... and as you continue to use Reiki as a principal aspect of your daily self care, it will not disappoint. But, this is me speaking ... **perhaps it is time for *you* to discover Reiki for yourself!**

With the healing blessings of Self-Care Reiki and all that is, and in the Divine energy of the presence of now, may I say one last time ... please be gentle with yourself as you move forward in this day and in this special and beautiful life you are living, in deep gratitude.

Thank you for sharing your time with me during your reading of this book. It has been my absolute pleasure to have you accompany me as I have been writing these words for and to you!

Namaste! I bow to the Divine in you!!

Judith

A Quick Review

Simply stated: *What is Reiki?*

Reiki is energy!

The longer answer?

* *Reiki is healing energy,*
* *Reiki is meditation,*
* *Reiki is peace,*
* *Reiki is love and compassion,*
* *Reiki is gratitude,*
* *Reiki is a way of being,*
* *Reiki is mindfulness training,*
* *Reiki is our relationship with ourselves, with one another and with the Universe,*
* *Reiki is an energy that is alive, that heals, that awakens when we open ourselves to it,*
* *Reiki is an energy that guides ... guides us **through** our opening awareness **towards** those things we need, and **away from** those things that may be harmful,*
* *Reiki is life-changing,*
* *Reiki guides us to live in the presence of now.*

What is happening when we place our hands on our body?

Our natural and positive energy is stimulated to flow.

Can we move energy in our body without placing our hands on our body?

Yes!

How?

* By thinking positively *in all we do, in all we are and in all we can be.*

- By acting positively *in all we do, in all we are and in all we can be.*
- By living positively *in all we do, in all we are and in all we can be.*

Is this realistic?

It is a choice we can each make, one situation at a time, *in the presence of now!*

Could we also refer to Reiki as 'Divine flow' of energy within our body?

Yes ... if our concept of 'Divine' suggests all that is natural and positive in the Universe. **Reiki is not religion. Nor is it a belief system.** Reiki is an opening into the reality of what can be when you connect with and live from awareness of something more in your life. So the word 'Divine' is used here to describe its qualities that are beyond human intelligence.

What removes us from Reiki energy flow?

Such things as:

- Not wanting to move outside our 'comfort level.'
- Life's situations and surprises that we interpret negatively.
- Forgetting we are always able to re-connect to Reiki energy flow, despite life's disappointments and tragedies.

Do we have control over this?

Yes!

How?

By remaining connected through a daily self-care practice with Reiki energy 'flow' throughout all our responses to life's unexpected issues.

Does this mean that we can either be in the 'Reiki flow' or in some other kind of flow such as 'worry flow,' 'anger flow' or 'critical flow,' etc.?

Yes!

Then ... *could we* — at the moment of awareness of our worry, anger or fear, etc. — ask ourselves the simple question: *Do I want to be in the worry flow or the Reiki flow? ... the anger flow or the Reiki flow?... the critical flow or the Reiki flow? ... etc.*

Yes!

And if we choose the Reiki flow, *can we bring ourselves back into an awareness of healthy energy flow again?*

Yes!

Would this be life changing?

Monumental! Yes!

Does it happen automatically?

No!

How do we train ourselves to make this simple choice?

The Reiki Precepts teach us to become mindful of the times we are not in the flow of Reiki energy, by mindfully:

* **assessing how we feel in the presence of now** — positive or negative; by

* **mindfully training ourselves to become aware that we have a choice of how to react in the presence of now,** by reacting through anger, worry, or compassion, as examples; and by

* **choosing to let go of whatever angst we are carrying** that prevents our being in the Reiki flow; and by

* **choosing to think and behave in a positive manner** — allowing a positive flow of energy to return; releasing negativity ... the source of much dysfunction in our lives.

Then, by

* **embracing the positive energy flow of Reiki** instead of worry,

* **embracing the positive energy flow of Reiki** instead of anger,

* **embracing the positive energy flow of Reiki** instead of criticism,

* **embracing the positive energy flow of Reiki** instead of fear, resentment, etc.

The Precepts teach us to mindfully become compassionate with ourselves and with others. Learning to become compassionate with the one who creates resentment or anger within you, causes you to stop and consider the person from a compassionate viewpoint of what they might be feeling or going through, instead of focusing solely on one's egocentric reaction to their behaviour. *Compassion is the loving energy of a Reiki energy connection. Compassion contains the 'light' energies of love and peace.* It stimulates Reiki energy to flow in your body and mind and can completely alter the outcome of what might normally be an 'incident,' that creates bad will and subsequent 'dark' and long-lasting estrangement energies in relationships.

The Precepts in their original wording were as follows:

Just for today, do not worry
Just for today, do not anger
Honour your parents, teachers and elders
Earn your living honestly
Show gratitude to every living thing.

The Precepts are timeless, applying to everyday life of any era. In this book, we have taken Precepts three and four and modernized the wording, by introducing the word 'compassion' ... reminding us to show ourselves compassion as well as others. In Precept four, we have used the word 'truth,' so that it is broader in context to live an entire way of life in truth ... being authentic in all we do and are.

Can Self-Care Reiki be used for physical conditions as well as emotional situations?

Reiki may help in three ways:

First, if a physical condition is creating stress or has been caused by stress, **Self-Care Reiki touch can help to ease the way that the person is experiencing the stress by offering**

temporary relaxation. If the stress is relieved, the physical condition may also be decreased or even eliminated.

Second, when the individual is more relaxed, the symptoms of the physical condition such as pain, may be reduced.

Third, and this is the most critical from the perspective of a public health nurse *(aka myself)*, whose raison d'être is prevention! **Self-Care Reiki touch plus Precepts can prevent many conditions that have stress as a basic cause.** By learning how to reduce or eliminate stress, we are keeping our body's energy flowing freely, such that it can defend and heal itself in the presence of potential threats.

Why do you refer to Self-Care Reiki Meditation throughout this book?

I want to impress upon readers that by using your self-care practice as a form of meditation in the ways I am suggesting, you are going to benefit more from the practice of self-care touch, since meditation engages your mind as well as your hands. You will find in the way you feel following a Self-Care Reiki Meditation session, that it also engages your emotions. And all of this will nourish your soul and liberate your spirit ... a greater return on investment for time spent in self care!

Can Self-Care Reiki Meditation plus Precepts benefit one's overall health?

The short answer is yes! For example, when you feel stressed, a hand placed on your heart centre combined with the slowing of the breath, can bring almost immediate relief.

The longer answer?

As review ... to receive the most benefit from a Self-Care Reiki practice, time needs to be reserved in your day to do this. You can place your hands on your body as you watch TV, and **you will receive physical benefit in terms of relaxation.**

Or, you can place your hands on your body and turn off the TV! Create a special space in your home or outdoors, or both, to practice self care. Turn on quiet meditation music or enjoy the sounds of your environment. Light a candle to create a sense of peace for your self-care time. This will change your hands-on practice to a time of Self-Care Reiki Meditation, by intentionally slowing your breath ... expanding your lungs with each breath and allowing more oxygen to enter your lungs ... feeling your body relax as you breathe more slowly ... allowing your mind to become quieter and your emotions calmer.

When the physical part of your Self-Care Reiki practice is done in this manner, you are training your body to become quieter and calmer. The Precepts train the mind to become quieter. This combination of self-care tools contributes to improved physical, mental and emotional health and wellbeing.

On a physical level, you are stimulating a greater energy flow when you breathe more slowly and deeply. Relaxation is a huge benefit of a Self-Care Reiki practice, leading to reduced stress, in general. (A good example of this is hypertension. For those with a pre-disposition to this condition, a Self-Care Reiki practice in all its forms especially including the Precepts, may keep you in a de-stressed way of being and your blood pressure recording at safer levels. The effect of this, is to reduce your potential for cardiac-related complications of hypertension.) Indeed **all the benefits of a meditation practice can be attributed to Self-Care Reiki when Reiki is conducted in a meditative manner.**

And for those who cannot find the time in your day to do an intentional meditative Self-Care Reiki session, then **simply place your hands on the sides of your chest while lying in bed at night and intentionally slow your breath ... this will ascribe helpful benefits, one of which might be relaxing you more quickly to fall asleep.**

What is the role of gratitude in health?

Gratitude is a game changer ... it's the ability to see the half full rather than half empty glass concept in everything. It's about learning to say "Yes!" to new ideas and allow them to be heard and experienced. It's about 'feeling' thankful, genuinely, in the presence of now, for all that constitutes your life ... looking for the positives instead of focusing on the negative ...then allowing those positives to grow. It's about taking the time to notice and to comment positively, in the presence of now, when something very simple, yet wonderful, happens before your eyes, rather than ignoring it. On its own, the practice of showing gratitude to every living thing, will change your life.

Summary

Self-Care Reiki practiced daily becomes 'lifestyle.' It influences everything you do and how you do it. It leads you closer to a sense of wellbeing, and returns you to your authentic self — if you have strayed from this — and from your inner home of love, compassion and peace. In fact, inner peace, in the presence of now amidst chaos, or Anshin Ritsumei, is the ultimate goal of a Self-Care Reiki practice.

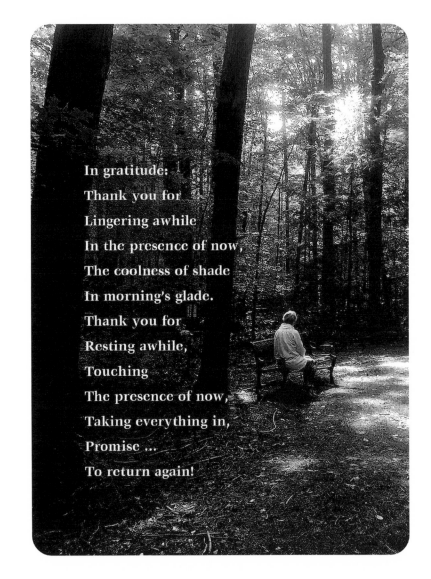

In gratitude:
Thank you for
Lingering awhile
In the presence of now,
The coolness of shade
In morning's glade.
Thank you for
Resting awhile,
Touching
The presence of now,
Taking everything in,
Promise ...
To return again!

Imagine what the Universe, unified in you, can do ...

ABOUT THE AUTHOR

 Judith's life work has been in the preventative health care field as a community public health nurse, regional home care program assistant director, and corporate occupational health medical and nursing manager. Currently, Judith, as wellness facilitator and author, leads courses and women's retreats on the subject of body, mind and spirit wellness directed towards raising student awareness of a lifestyle of prevention and fulfillment that arises from a balanced way of being. She has been teaching Self-Care Reiki Wellness since 1996, and has volunteered as a Reiki practitioner for Hospice Care Ottawa since 2010, seeing family members, staff and residents, on referral. Judith is also a teacher with the Insight Timer Meditation App, where she offers several guided meditations and two courses, titled: *Self-Care Healing Spaces of Grief and Loss* and *Living the Presence of Now with Self-Care Reiki*. All of her published work is available on the internet.

ABOUT THE YOGA INSTRUCTOR

 Louise Murray is an experienced yoga teacher. She obtained her teaching certification from the International Sivananda Vedanta Center in 2000, and has been teaching on a regular basis until March 2020. Over the years she completed her training in Yoga of the Heart, Yin, Restorative and Yoga for Seniors. Her commitment to her own regular practice of yoga and meditation since the early 90's, has helped her maintain a sense of balance, strength and total well-being in her daily life. She lives in Carp, Ontario, Canada.

ENDNOTES.

1 David E McManus, PhD, *Reiki is Better Than Placebo and Has Broad Potential as a Complementary Therapy*, Journal of Evidence-Based Complementary & Alternative Medicine, Oct, 2017, https://www.ncbi.nlm.nih.gov/pmc/articles/PMC5871310/.

2 John O'Donohue, *Benedictus, A Book of Blessings*, "For One Who Is Exhausted," Bantam Press, UK, 2007, p141.

3 Eckhart Tolle, *The Power of Now*, Random House, 2005.

4 Distance of Earth from Sun, 94.499 million miles. www.nasa.gov.

5 Richard Bach, *Jonathon Livingston Seagull, A Story*, The MacMillan Company, New York, 1970, p 63.

6 Hiroshi Doi, *A Modern Reiki Method for Healing*, Vision Publications, Southfield, MI, Revised Edition, 2014.

7 Frans Stiene, *Reiki Insights*, O-Books, John Hunt Publishing Ltd., Hampshire, UK, 2018.

8 Insight Timer is a free app you can download or visit their website: www.insighttimer.com.

9 Steve Gold, *Golden OM*, Insight Timer, insighttimer.com, "Golden OM is intended to inspire deep relaxation and exalted creativity."

10 Meditation — Christopher Plowman, "Building A Future For Insight Timer & The Planet," in conversation with Ed Andrew of Human Impact Podcast, available on Insight Timer, 2019.

11 Phyllis Furomoto, *On-Line Commentary from Global Webinar*, 2016 (approx.).

12 Judith M Campbell, *I Brake for Butterflies*, General Store Publishing House, 2006, p xl.

13 Judith Campbell, *Reiki Presence*, Insight Timer, 2017: https://insighttimer.com/judithcampbell.

14 A Reiki attunement is a ritual performed by a certified, teaching Reiki Master to strengthen energy flow in a student of Reiki teachings.

15 John O'Donohue, *Benedictus, A Book of Blessings,* "For One Who Is Exhausted," Bantam Press, UK, 2007, p141.

16 Sonic Yoga, *Root Chakra Singing Bowls with Binaural Beat,* 2012.

17 Lilias Folan, *Yoga Gets Better with Age,* Rodale Inc., USA, distributed by HoltzBrinck publishers, 2005, p 174.

18 Ibid.

19 Ibid.

20 William Shakespeare, *Hamlet,* "Act 1, Scene 3," (spoken by King Claudius) https://www.williamshakespeare.net/hamlet.jsp.

21 Sonic Yoga, *Sacral Chakra Tibetan Singing Bowl,* Insight Timer, 2012.

22 Snatum Kaur, *Beloved,* "Sat Naaraa-In," Spirit Voyage Records, 2018.

23 blog.spiritvoyage.com

24 PabloArellano, *Deep Peace Guitar,* Insight Timer, rated 4.9/5 stars.

25 These words are taken from the Terms of Reference of Hospice Care Ottawa's broad definition of Spirituality, Ottawa, Canada, 2016.

26 Sonic Yogi, *Heart Chakra Tibetan Singing Bowls,* Insight Timer, 2018.

27 These words are taken from the Terms of Reference of Hospice Care Ottawa's broad definition of Spirituality, Ottawa, Canada, 2016.

28 Eithne L Barker, *Come Rise to the Rhythm of My Soul,* June 10, 2010.

29 Sonic Yoga, *Throat Chakra Tibetan Singing Bowls with Ocean Sounds,* Insight Timer, 2018.

30 Suzanne Teng, *Enchanted Wind,* "Above the Clouds," Autumn Light Productions,(C) Suzanne Teng, 2006.

31 Eithne L. Barker, *Come Rise to the Rhythm of My Soul*, June 10, 2010.

32 A Furuyashiki, K Tabuchi, K Norikoshi, *A Comparative Study of the Physiological and Psychological Effects of Forest Bathing*, published online, June 22, 2019, https://www.natureandforesttherapy.org/about/science.

33 Suzanne Teng, *Mystic Journey*, "Lotus," Autumn Light Productions, 2008.

34 Pablo Arellano, *Whispering Notes*, Insight Timer.

35 Bill Howatt, *Workplace stress a main cause of mental health issues, study finds*, (Bill Howell is the chief research and development officer of work force productivity with Morneau Shepell in Toronto, Canada) *Globe and Mail*, July 5, 2018.

36 Cindy Black, *Meridian Massage*, "Opening Pathways to Vitality," Copyright © 2016, Cindy Black, *Shen Men*, "Spirit Gate," p111.

37 Judith Campbell, *Reiki Meditation for Peaceful Sleep*, Insight Timer, 2017.

38 Kevin James, *The Peaceful Heart / Shakuhachi Flute with Crystal Bowls*, Insight Timer, 2019.

39 Mayo Clinic Staff, *The Benefits of Relaxation Techniques, Relaxation Techniques*: "Try These to Reduce Stress," https://www.mayoclinic.org/healthy-lifestyle/stress-management/in-depth/relaxation-technique/art-20045368.

40 Arielle Schwartz, *The Parasympathetic Nervous System and Your Health, Somatic Resilience*, March 11, 2019, https://drarielleschwartz.com/the-parasympathetic-nervous-system-and-your-health/#.XwicwyHPxbU.

41 Xiaolan Zhao, CMD, *Inner Beauty: Looking, Feeling and Being Your Best Through Traditional Chinese Medicine*, Random House Canada, 2011, p 279.

42 The Wong Janice, *Cello Music for Sleep*, or *Cello for Your Soul*: "Ecstasy," Insight Timer, 2020.

43 Judith Campbell, *The Reiki Breath of Peace Meditation*, Insight Timer, 2016. (You might wish to try this meditation for times of needing to breathe the Reiki breath of peace.)